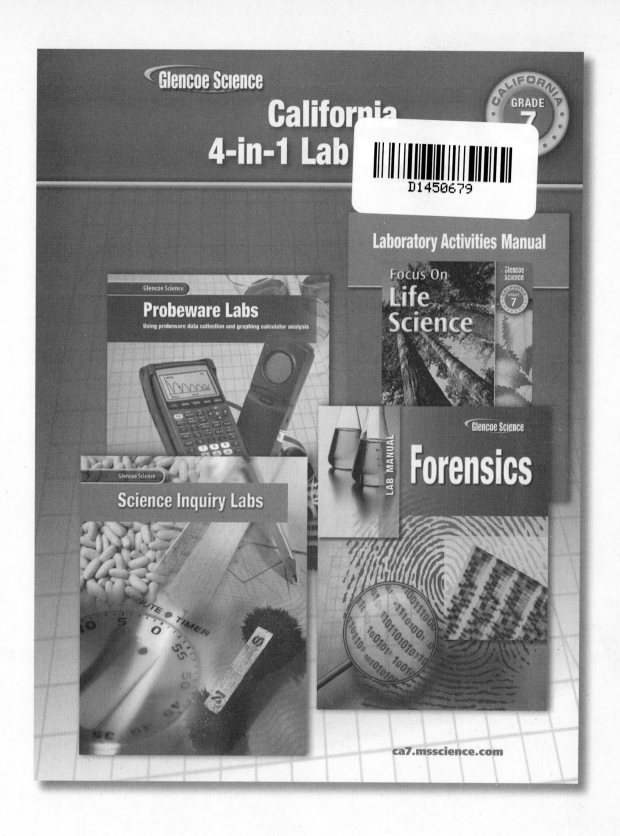

Glencoe Science

CALIFORNIA GRADE 7

California 4-in-1 Lab

D1450679

Laboratory Activities Manual

Glencoe Science
Probeware Labs
Using probeware data collection and graphing calculator analysis

Focus On
Life Science

Glencoe Science
CALIFORNIA GRADE 7

Glencoe Science
Science Inquiry Labs

LAB MANUAL
Glencoe Science
Forensics

ca7.msscience.com

Glencoe

New York, New York   Columbus, Ohio   Chicago, Illinois   Peoria, Illinois   Woodland Hills, California

Glencoe Science

Credits

The photo of the CBL 2, graphing calculator, and pH probe on the front cover and at the top of the first page of each student lab appears courtesy of Texas Instruments, Inc. Each Probeware Activity was reviewed by Richard Sorensen of Vernier Software & Technology.

The terms CBL 2, TI-GRAPH LINK, TI Connect and TI InterActive! are either registered trademarks of, trademarks of, or copyrighted by Texas Instruments, Inc. Vernier LabPro is a registered trademark of Graphical Analysis and EasyData copyrighted by Vernier Software & Technology. Macintosh is a registered trademark of Apple Computer, Inc. Windows is a registered trademark of Microsoft Corporation in the United States and/or other countries.

 Glencoe

Send all inquiries to:
Glencoe/McGraw-Hill
8787 Orion Place
Columbus, OH 43240

ISBN-13: 978-0-07-875488-3
ISBN-10: 0-07-875488-7

Printed in the United States of America.

1 2 3 4 5 6 7 8 9 10 071 11 10 09 08 07 06

Table of Contents

LABORATORY ACTIVITIES

To the Student

Glencoe's 4-in-1 Lab Manual provides you with four separate sections of labs. While each section is unique, all the lab activities in this manual require your active participation. You will test hypotheses, collect and apply data, and discover new information. You will use many different skills to make connections between the lab activities and what you already know.

The *Laboratory Activities* will help you focus your efforts on gathering information, obtaining data from the environment, and making observations. You will also work on organizing your data so conclusions can be drawn in a way that is easily repeated by other scientists.

The *Inquiry Activities* will help you understand that no science works alone. A scientist cannot explain how a plant makes food just by knowing the parts of the leaf. Someone needs to know how the chemicals in the leaf work. Knowledge of Earth science, life science, and physical science is needed for a full explanation of how the leaf makes food. Today, teams of scientists solve problems. Each scientist uses his or her knowledge of Earth science, life science, or physical science to find solutions to problems in areas such as the environment or health.

The *Forensics Activities* provide in-depth investigations that deal with DNA, collecting and analyzing data, and interpreting evidence found at a crime or accident scene. You will use your knowledge of scientific inquiry and your problem-solving skills as you learn about forensics procedures. You will then apply these procedures to real-world scenarios.

The *Probeware Activities* are designed to help you study science using probeware technology. A probeware lab is different from other labs because it uses a probe or sensor to collect data, a data collection unit to interpret and store the data, and a graphing calculator or computer to analyze the data. These components are connected with a software program called DataMate that makes them work together in an easy-to-use, handheld system. These labs are designed specifically for the TI-73 or TI-83 Plus graphing calculators and a CBL 2™ (produced by Texas Instruments, Inc.) or LabPro® (produced by Vernier Software & Technology) data collection unit.

Getting Started

Science is the body of information including all the hypotheses and experiments that tell us about our environment. All people involved in scientific work use similar methods for gaining information. One important scientific skill is the ability to obtain data directly from the environment. Observations must be based on what occurs in the environment. Equally important is the ability to organize these data into a form from which valid conclusions can be drawn. These conclusions must be such that other scientists can achieve the same results in the laboratory.

To make the most of your laboratory experience, you need to continually work to increase your laboratory skills. These skills include the ability to recognize and use equipment properly and to measure and use SI units accurately. Safety must also be an ongoing concern. To help you get started in discovering many fascinating things about the world around you, the next few pages provide you with the following:

- a visual overview of basic **laboratory equipment** for you to label
- a reference sheet of **safety symbols**
- a list of your **safety responsibilities** in the laboratory
- a **safety contract**
- a reference sheet of **SI units**

Each lab activity in this manual includes the following sections:

- an investigation **title** and introductory section providing information about the problem under study
- a **strategy** section identifying the **objective(s)** of the activity
- a list of needed **materials**
- safety concerns identified with **safety icons** and **caution statements**
- a set of step-by-step **procedures**
- a section to help you record your **data and observations**
- a section to help you **analyze your data** and record your **conclusions**
- a closing **strategy check** so that you can review your achievement of the objectives of the activity

Laboratory Equipment

Figure 1

1. _____

2. _____

3. _____

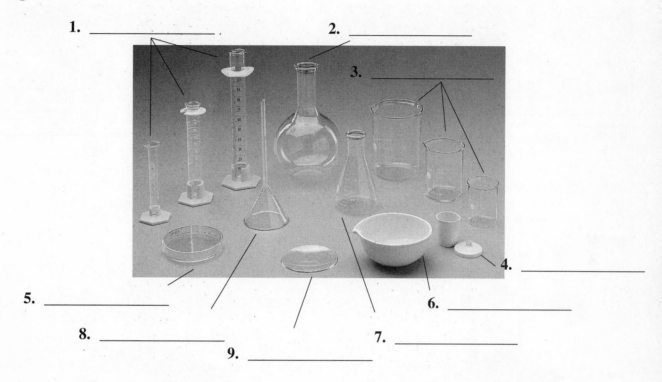

4. _____

5. _____

6. _____

7. _____

8. _____

9. _____

Figure 2

1. _____

2. _____

3. _____

4. _____

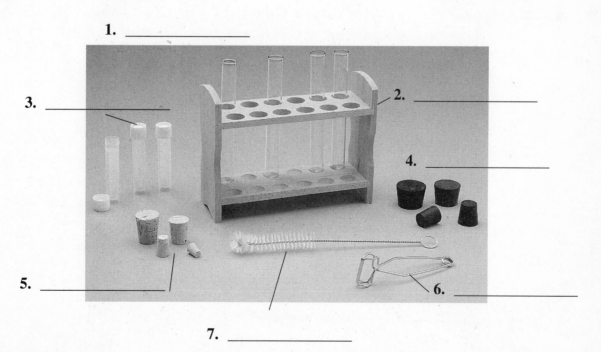

5. _____

6. _____

7. _____

Laboratory Equipment (continued)

Figure 3

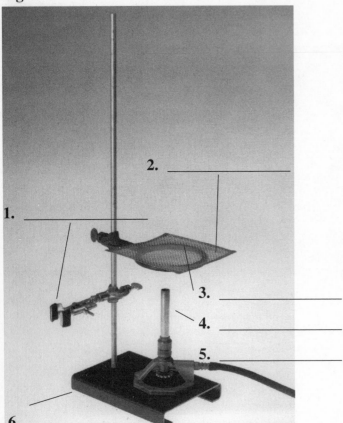

1. _____
2. _____
3. _____
4. _____
5. _____
6. _____

Figure 4

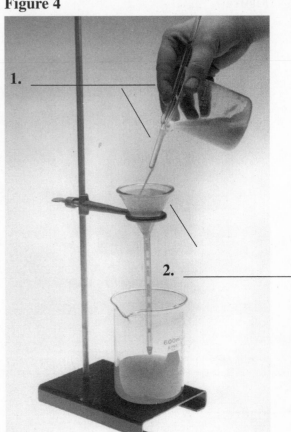

1. _____
2. _____

Figure 5

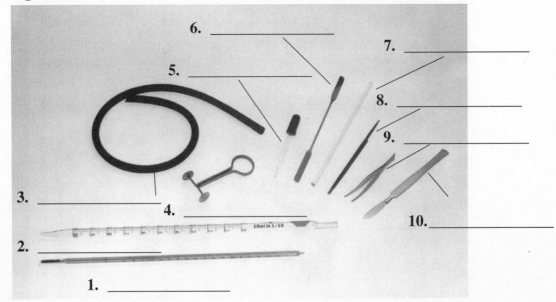

1. _____
2. _____
3. _____
4. _____
5. _____
6. _____
7. _____
8. _____
9. _____
10. _____

Laboratory Equipment (continued)

Figure 6

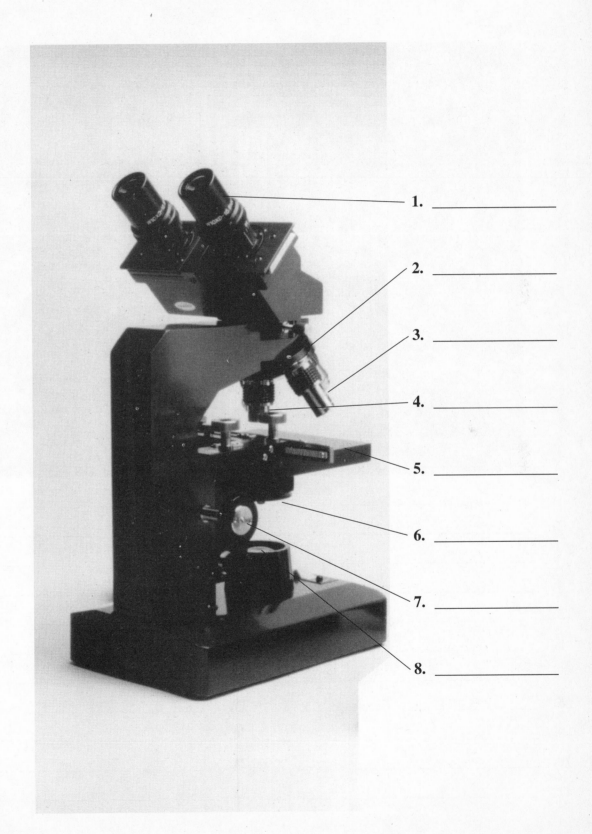

1. _____

2. _____

3. _____

4. _____

5. _____

6. _____

7. _____

8. _____

Laboratory Equipment (continued)

Figure 7

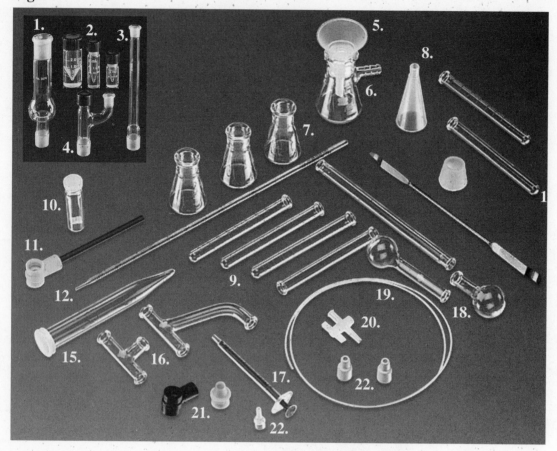

1. _____
2. _____
3. _____
4. _____
5. _____
6. _____
7. _____
8. _____
9. _____
10. _____
11. _____

12. _____
13. _____
14. _____
15. _____
16. _____
17. _____
18. _____
19. _____
20. _____
21. _____
22. _____

Laboratory Equipment (continued)

Figure 8

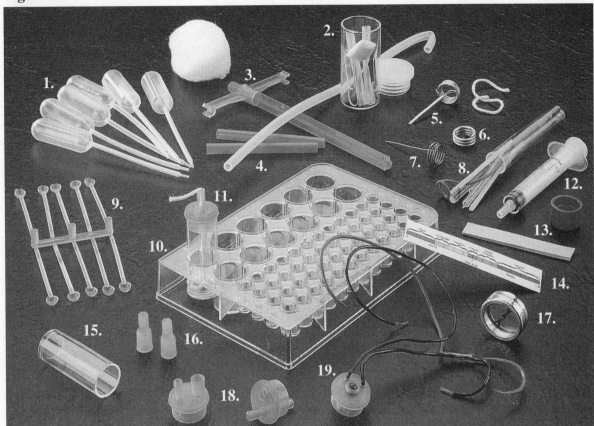

1. _____	11. _____
2. _____	12. _____
3. _____	13. _____
4. _____	14. _____
5. _____	15. _____
6. _____	16. _____
7. _____	17. _____
8. _____	18. _____
9. _____	19. _____
10. _____	

SAFETY SYMBOLS

SAFETY SYMBOLS	HAZARD	EXAMPLES	PRECAUTION	REMEDY
DISPOSAL	Special disposal procedures need to be followed.	certain chemicals, living organisms	Do not dispose of these materials in the sink or trash can.	Dispose of wastes as directed by your teacher.
BIOLOGICAL	Organisms or other biological materials that might be harmful to humans	bacteria, fungi, blood, unpreserved tissues, plant materials	Avoid skin contact with these materials. Wear mask or gloves.	Notify your teacher if you suspect contact with material. Wash hands thoroughly.
EXTREME TEMPERATURE	Objects that can burn skin by being too cold or too hot	boiling liquids, hot plates, dry ice, liquid nitrogen	Use proper protection when handling.	Go to your teacher for first aid.
SHARP OBJECT	Use of tools or glassware that can easily puncture or slice skin	razor blades, pins, scalpels, pointed tools, dissecting probes, broken glass	Practice common-sense behavior and follow guidelines for use of the tool.	Go to your teacher for first aid.
FUME	Possible danger to respiratory tract from fumes	ammonia, acetone, nail polish remover, heated sulfur, moth balls	Make sure there is good ventilation. Never smell fumes directly. Wear a mask.	Leave foul area and notify your teacher immediately.
ELECTRICAL	Possible danger from electrical shock or burn	improper grounding, liquid spills, short circuits, exposed wires	Double-check setup with teacher. Check condition of wires and apparatus.	Do not attempt to fix electrical problems. Notify your teacher immediately.
IRRITANT	Substances that can irritate the skin or mucous membranes of the respiratory tract	pollen, moth balls, steel wool, fiberglass, potassium permanganate	Wear dust mask and gloves. Practice extra care when handling these materials.	Go to your teacher for first aid.
CHEMICAL	Chemicals can react with and destroy tissue and other materials	bleaches such as hydrogen peroxide; acids such as sulfuric acid, hydrochloric acid; bases such as ammonia, sodium hydroxide	Wear goggles, gloves, and an apron.	Immediately flush the affected area with water and notify your teacher.
TOXIC	Substance may be poisonous if touched, inhaled, or swallowed.	mercury, many metal compounds, iodine, poinsettia plant parts	Follow your teacher's instructions.	Always wash hands thoroughly after use. Go to your teacher for first aid.
FLAMMABLE	Flammable chemicals may be ignited by open flame, spark, or exposed heat.	alcohol, kerosene, potassium permanganate	Avoid open flames and heat when using flammable chemicals.	Notify your teacher immediately. Use fire safety equipment if applicable.
OPEN FLAME	Open flame in use, may cause fire.	hair, clothing, paper, synthetic materials	Tie back hair and loose clothing. Follow teacher's instruction on lighting and extinguishing flames.	Notify your teacher immediately. Use fire safety equipment if applicable.

 Eye Safety Proper eye protection should be worn at all times by anyone performing or observing science activities.

 Clothing Protection This symbol appears when substances could stain or burn clothing.

 Animal Safety This symbol appears when safety of animals and students must be ensured.

 Handwashing After the lab, wash hands with soap and water before removing goggles.

Student Laboratory and Safety Guidelines

Regarding Emergencies

- Inform the teacher immediately of *any* mishap—fire, injury, glassware breakage, chemical spills, etc.
- Follow your teacher's instructions and your school's procedures in dealing with emergencies.

Regarding Your Person

- Do NOT wear clothing that is loose enough to catch on anything, and avoid sandals or open-toed shoes.
- Wear protective safety gloves, goggles, and aprons as instructed.
- Always wear safety goggles (not glasses) when using hazardous chemicals.
- Wear goggles throughout the entire activity, cleanup, and handwashing.
- Keep your hands away from your face while working in the laboratory.
- Remove synthetic fingernails before working in the lab (these are highly flammable).
- Do NOT use hair spray, mousse, or other flammable hair products just before or during laboratory work where an open flame is used (they can ignite easily).
- Tie back long hair and loose clothing to keep them away from flames and equipment.
- Remove loose jewelry—chains or bracelets—while doing lab work.
- NEVER eat or drink while in the lab or store food in lab equipment or the lab refrigerator.
- Do NOT inhale vapors or taste, touch, or smell any chemical or substance unless instructed to do so by your teacher.

Regarding Your Work

- Read all instructions before you begin a laboratory or field activity. Ask questions if you do not understand any part of the activity.
- Work ONLY on activities assigned by your teacher.
- Do NOT substitute other chemicals/substances for those listed in your activity.
- Do NOT begin any activity until directed to do so by your teacher.
- Do NOT handle any equipment without specific permission.
- Remain in your own work area unless given permission by your teacher to leave it.
- Do NOT point heated containers—test tubes, flasks, etc.—at yourself or anyone else.
- Do NOT take any materials or chemicals out of the classroom.
- Stay out of storage areas unless you are instructed to be there and are supervised by your teacher.
- NEVER work alone in the laboratory.
- When using dissection equipment, always cut away from yourself and others. Cut downward, never stabbing at the object.
- Handle living organisms or preserved specimens only when authorized by your teacher.
- Always wear heavy gloves when handling animals. If you are bitten or stung, notify your teacher immediately.

Regarding Cleanup

- Keep work and lab areas clean, limiting the amount of easily ignitable materials.
- Turn off all burners and other equipment before leaving the lab.
- Carefully dispose of waste materials as instructed by your teacher.
- Wash your hands thoroughly with soap and warm water after each activity.

Student Science Laboratory Safety Contract

I agree to:

- Act responsibly at all times in the laboratory.

- Follow all instructions given, orally or in writing, by my teacher.

- Perform only those activities assigned and approved by my teacher.

- Protect my eyes, face, hands, and body by wearing proper clothing and using protective equipment provided by my school.

- Carry out good housekeeping practices as instructed by my teacher.

- Know the location of safety and first-aid equipment in the laboratory.

- Notify my teacher immediately of an emergency.

- NEVER work alone in the laboratory.

- NEVER eat or drink in the laboratory unless instructed to do so by my teacher.

- Handle living organisms or preserved specimens only when authorized by my teacher, and then, with respect.

- NEVER enter or work in a supply area unless instructed to do so and supervised by my teacher.

[This portion of the contract is to be kept by the student.]

- -

[Return this portion to your teacher.]

I, _____, [print name] have read each of the statements in the Student Science Laboratory Safety Contract and understand these safety rules. I agree to abide by the safety regulations and any additional written or verbal instructions provided by the school district or my teacher. I further agree to follow all other written and verbal instructions given in class.

_____   _____
                 Student Signature   Date

I acknowledge that my child/ward has signed this contract in good faith.

_____   _____
           Parent/Guardian Signature   Date

SI Reference Sheet

The International System of Units (SI) is accepted as the standard for measurement throughout most of the world. Sometimes quantities are measured using different SI units. In order to use them together in an equation, you must convert all of the quantities into the same unit. To convert, you multiply by a conversion factor. A conversion factor is a ratio that is equal to one. Make a conversion factor by building a ratio of equivalent units. Place the new units in the numerator and the old units in the denominator. For example, to convert 1.255 L to mL, multiply 1.255 L by the appropriate ratio as follows:

$$1.255 \text{ L} \times 1{,}000 \text{ mL}/1 \text{ L} = 1{,}255 \text{ mL}$$

In this equation, the unit L cancels just as if it were a number.

Frequently used SI units are listed in **Table 1.**

Table 1

Frequently Used SI Units	
Length	1 millimeter (mm) = 100 micrometers (μm) 1 centimeter (cm) = 10 millimeters (mm) 1 meter (m) = 100 centimeters (cm) 1 kilometer (km) = 1,000 meters (m) 1 light-year = 9,460,000,000,000 kilometers (km)
Area	1 square meter (m²) = 10,000 square centimeters (cm²) 1 square kilometer (km²) = 1,000,000 square meters (m²)
Volume	1 milliliter (mL) = 1 cubic centimeter (cm³) 1 liter (L) = 1,000 milliliters (mL)
Mass	1 gram (g) = 1,000 milligrams (mg) 1 kilogram (kg) = 1,000 grams (g) 1 metric ton = 1,000 kilograms (kg)
Time	1 s = 1 second

Several other supplementary SI units are listed in **Table 2.**

Table 2

Supplementary SI Units			
Measurement	**Unit**	**Symbol**	**Expressed in base units**
Energy	joule	J	$kg \cdot m^2/s^2$
Force	newton	N	$kg \cdot m/s^2$
Power	watt	W	$kg \cdot m^2/s^3$ or J/s
Pressure	pascal	Pa	$kg/m \cdot s^2$ or $N \cdot m$

Temperature measurements in SI often are made in degrees Celsius. Celsius temperature is a supplementary unit derived from the base unit kelvin. The Celsius scale (°C) has 100 equal graduations between the freezing temperature (0°C) and the boiling temperature of water (100°C). The following relationship exists between the Celsius and kelvin temperature scales:

$$K = °C + 273$$

Figure 1

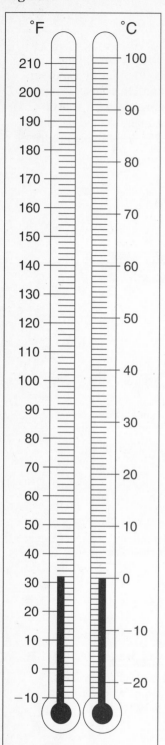

To convert from °F to °C, you can:

1. For exact amounts, use the equation at the bottom of **Table 3**

OR

2. For approximate amounts, find °F on the thermometer at the left of **Figure 1** and determine °C on the thermometer at the right.

Table 3

SI Metric to English Conversions			
	When you want to convert:	**Multiply by:**	**To find:**
Length	inches	2.54	centimeters
	centimeters	0.39	inches
	feet	0.30	meters
	meters	3.28	feet
	yards	0.91	meters
	meters	1.09	yards
	miles	1.61	kilometers
	kilometers	0.62	miles
Mass and weight*	ounces	28.35	grams
	grams	0.04	ounces
	pounds	0.45	kilograms
	kilograms	2.20	pounds
	tons	0.91	metric tons
	metric tons	1.10	tons
	pounds	4.45	newtons
	newtons	0.23	pounds
Volume	cubic inches	16.39	cubic centimeters
	milliliters	0.06	cubic inches
	cubic feet	0.03	cubic meters
	cubic meters	35.31	cubic feet
	liters	1.06	quarts
	liters	0.26	gallons
	gallons	3.78	liters
Area	square inches	6.45	square centimeters
	square centimeters	0.16	square inches
	square feet	0.09	square meters
	square meters	10.76	square feet
	square miles	2.59	square kilometers
	square kilometers	0.39	square miles
	hectares	2.47	acres
	acres	0.40	hectares
Temperature	Fahrenheit	$\frac{5}{9}(°F - 32)$	Celsius
	Celsius	$\frac{9}{5}°C + 32$	Fahrenheit

* Weight as measured in standard Earth gravity

Laboratory Activities

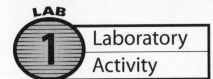

The Compound Light Microscope

A microscope is a scientific tool used to see very small objects. Objects you cannot see with your eyes alone can be seen using a microscope. In this experiment, you will look at a small letter *e* cut from a magazine, some thread, and a strand of hair using a compound light microscope.

Strategy

You will learn the names of the parts of a compound light microscope.

You will learn how to use a compound light microscope.

You will learn to prepare objects for viewing under a compound light microscope.

You will examine several objects under a compound light microscope.

You will determine how the lens system of a compound light microscope changes the position of an object being viewed.

Materials

microscope   coverslip   water   nylon thread

scissors   dropper   strands of hair   wool thread

magazine

Procedure

Part A—Using the Compound Light Microscope

1. Study Figure 1. Identify the parts of your microscope so that you will understand the directions for this activity.

2. Cut out a small letter *e* from a magazine and place the letter on a microscope slide. **WARNING:** *Use care when handling sharp objects.* Put a small drop of water on the letter and place a coverslip over the water and the letter.

3. Place the slide on the microscope stage. Move the slide to center the letter *e* over the hole in the stage. Use the stage clips to hold the slide in place.

4. Turn on the light if your microscope has one. **WARNING:** *Do not use direct sunlight as a light source. It can damage eyes.* If it does not, adjust the mirror so that the light is reflected through the eyepiece.

Figure 1

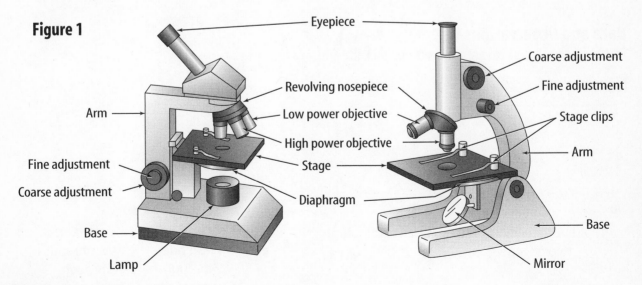

 SCI 7.a. Select and use appropriate tools and technology (including calculators, computers, balances, spring scales, microscopes, and binoculars) to perform tests, collect data, and display data.

Copyright © Glencoe/McGraw-Hill, a division of The McGraw-Hill Companies, Inc.

Laboratory Activity 1 (continued)

5. Look to see how the letter *e* is positioned on the slide before looking through the eyepiece. In the space for Figure 2a in Data and Observations, draw the letter as you see it without the aid of the microscope.

6. Click the low power objective lens (shortest, if more than one lens is present) into position. The lens should be directly over the hole in the stage. Bring the lens close to the slide using the coarse adjustment knob. NOTE: Be careful not to touch the slide with the lens. This might break the lens and the slide.

7. Look through the eyepiece of the microscope. Carefully bring the letter into focus by slowly turning the coarse adjustment knob. If you cannot see the letter, move the slide a little bit to be sure the letter is under the lens. If your microscope has only one objective lens, proceed directly to step 9; skip step 8.

8. Click the high power objective lens into place. If your microscope has a high power objective, it will also have a fine adjustment knob. Look through the eyepiece again. Carefully bring the letter *e* into focus by slowly turning the fine adjustment knob. NOTE: Never turn the coarse adjustment knob when the high power objective lens is in place.

Click the low power objective lens back into place before going on to step 9.

9. When the letter *e* is clearly visible, draw in Figure 2b the position of the letter as you see it through the microscope. Next, move the slide to the left as you look through the eyepiece. Note which way the letter appears to move. Move the slide forward. Note which way it appears to move now.

10. Remove the slide and clean it.

Part B—Preparing Microscope Slides

1. Place a drop of water on a clean glass slide. Put a strand of hair from your head and a hair from your forearm on the water drop. Place a coverslip over the drop of water and the two different strands of hair.

2. Observe the hair using the procedure you used in Part A to observe the letter *e*.

3. In the space for Figure 3a in Data and Observations, draw the two hair strands as they appear through the microscope. Label the hairs "head" and "arm." Notice which strand appears thicker and show this difference in your sketch.

4. Repeat Part B using a strand of nylon thread and a strand of wool thread. Draw and label the threads in Figure 3b in Data and Observations.

Data and Observations

In the spaces below, draw what you observed.

Figure 2

a
Letter *e* without microscope

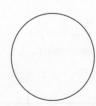

b
Letter *e* through microscope

Figure 3

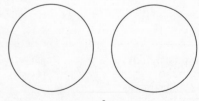

a
Arm and head hairs through microscope

b
Wool and nylon threads through microscope

Laboratory Activity 1 (continued)

Questions and Conclusions

1. Compare your drawing of the letter *e* without the microscope to your drawing of the letter seen through the microscope. Describe how the microscope changes the position of the letter.

   _____

   _____

   _____

2. In what direction does the slide under the microscope appear to move when you move it to the left?

   _____

   _____

3. Describe the differences in thickness you observed between arm hair and head hair.

   _____

   _____

   _____

4. Describe the differences you observed between wool thread and nylon thread.

   _____

   _____

   _____

5. What is the total magnification of your microscope? (Multiply the magnification of the eyepiece lens by the magnification of the objective lens. These numbers are printed on the lenses.)

   _____

   _____

6. Describe how you would correctly prepare a microscope slide of an insect wing for viewing under the microscope.

   _____

   _____

   _____

7. What precautions must be taken when using the high power lens?

   _____

   _____

   _____

Laboratory Activity 1 (continued)

8. From memory, correctly label the parts of the compound light microscope in Figure 4. (Turn to the Procedure only as a self-check.)

Figure 4

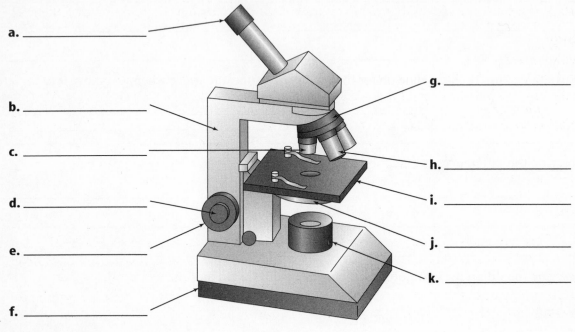

a. _____

b. _____

c. _____

d. _____

e. _____

f. _____

g. _____

h. _____

i. _____

j. _____

k. _____

Strategy Check

_____ Can you name the parts of a compound light microscope?

_____ Can you use a compound light microscope?

_____ Can you prepare slides of objects to be viewed under a compound light microscope?

_____ Can you examine an object under the compound light microscope?

_____ Can you explain how the lens system of your compound light microscope changes the position of any object as it is viewed through the eyepiece?

Observing Cells

If you were asked how a tree, a fly, and you are alike, you might answer, "We are all alive." If you could examine each under a microscope, you might answer, "We all contain cells." One very important similarity among all living things is that each is made of very small units called cells.

Strategy

You will prepare living things for microscopic viewing.
You will see that each living thing is made of cells and be able to name the parts of a cell.
You will compare plant cells to animal cells.

Materials

water
dropper
microscope slide

forceps
cork shavings
coverslip

microscope
lettuce leaf

prepared slide of
frog blood

Procedure

Part A—Observing Cork Cells

1. Add a drop of water to a clean microscope slide. Use forceps to add a small piece of cork. Cover with a coverslip.
2. View the cork under low power magnification. Change to high power if your microscope has a high power lens.
3. Draw what you observe under Data and Observations, Part A. Label what you see.

Part B—Observing Frog Blood Cells

1. View the prepared slide of frog blood under low power magnification. Change to high power if your microscope has a high power lens.
2. Draw what you observe under Data and Observations, Part B. Label the cell membrane, cytoplasm, and nucleus.

Part C—Observing Lettuce Leaf Cells

1. Add a drop of water to a clean microscope slide.
2. Remove a small piece of lettuce leaf and place it in the drop of water. Cover with a coverslip. Identify as many cell parts as you can.
3. Under Data and Observation, Part C, draw what you observe. Label the cell wall, chloroplast, cytoplasm, nucleus, and vacuoles. (The nucleus may be difficult to observe.)

Data and Observations

Figure 1

Part A

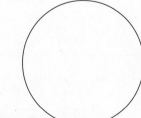

Part B

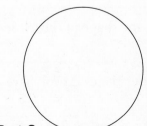

Part C

 SCI 1.b. Students know the characteristics that distinguish plant cells from animal cells, including chloroplasts and cell walls. Also covers **SCI 1.a.**

Copyright © Glencoe/McGraw-Hill, a division of The McGraw-Hill Companies, Inc.

Laboratory Activity 2 (continued)

Questions and Conclusions

1. Indicate if the words or phrases below refer to cork, frog blood, or lettuce leaf cells by circling the proper choice(s). More than one choice may be used for some phrases.

   a. not rectangular in shape   cork   frog blood   lettuce

   b. chloroplasts   cork   frog blood   lettuce

   c. vacuoles   cork   frog blood   lettuce

   d. cell wall   cork   frog blood   lettuce

   e. brick shape in appearance   cork   frog blood   lettuce

   f. nucleus   cork   frog blood   lettuce

   g. cytoplasm   cork   frog blood   lettuce

   h. no cell wall   cork   frog blood   lettuce

   i. an animal cell   cork   frog blood   lettuce

   j. a plant cell   cork   frog blood   lettuce

2. What do you call the small units in the cork that can be seen under high power?

   _____

   a. Do these units appear filled or empty?

   _____

   b. Is the cork produced by a plant or an animal? What evidence do you have?

   _____

3. Describe the shape of the frog blood cells.

   _____

   a. What is the outer edge of the frog blood cell called?

   _____

   b. What other parts are visible in the frog blood cell?

   _____

4. What is the shape of the lettuce leaf cell?

   _____

   a. What evidence do you have that lettuce is not made of animal cells?

   _____

   b. Where are the chloroplasts in a lettuce leaf cell?

   _____

Laboratory Activity 2 (continued)

5. List several parts that are found in both plant and animal cells.

   _____

   _____

6. What proof do you now have that living things are similar when viewed through a microscope?

   _____

   _____

7. Use your text to find and list the function of each of the following cell parts:
   a. cell wall

   _____

   _____

   b. chloroplast

   _____

   _____

   c. cytoplasm

   _____

   _____

   d. nucleus

   _____

   _____

   e. vacuole

   _____

   _____

   f. cell membrane

   _____

   _____

   g. endoplasmic reticulum

   _____

   _____

   h. mitochondria

   _____

   _____

Laboratory Activity 2 (continued)

8. Compare parts of a cell with parts of your school building. Match the cell part function with the function of the corresponding school area.

_____ cell wall	**a.** corridors
_____ nucleus	**b.** boiler room
_____ endoplasmic reticulum	**c.** cafeteria
_____ chloroplast	**d.** principal's office
_____ mitochondria	**e.** bricks of building

Strategy Check

_____ Can you prepare living things for microscopic viewing?

_____ Do you agree that all living things are made of cells?

_____ Can you correctly label those cell parts observed?

_____ Can you compare plant cells with animal cells?

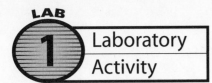

Root Structure and Functions

LAB 1 Laboratory Activity

Roots hold a plant in the ground. They also absorb, store, and transport water and minerals. They have small threadlike side roots with root hairs that absorb water and minerals from the soil. Taproots, such as carrots, have a primary root that grows straight down into the soil. Taproots look very different from fibrous roots, such as those on grasses, which have many small roots branching out in different directions.

Strategy
You will examine a dissected carrot root.
You will label a diagram of a root and list the function of each part.

Materials
carrot sliced crosswise
carrot sliced lengthwise
magnifying lens

Procedure
1. Your teacher will prepare a crosswise slice of a carrot for you.
2. Hold the slice up to the light. Compare what you see with Figure 1 under Data and Observations.
3. Examine the lengthwise slice of the carrot. Use the magnifying lens. Look at both the inner and outer parts.
4. The outside layer of the root is the epidermis. Lateral roots grow from the epidermal cells and root hairs grow from them. Label the epidermis, lateral roots, and root hairs if all of these structures are present.

5. Inside the epidermis, you will find several layers of large, loosely packed cells that store food. This is the cortex. Food stored in the cortex can be used by other cells of the plant. Label the cortex.
6. Inside the cortex are tubelike cells from xylem vessels that carry water and minerals in the plant. Label the xylem cells.
7. Other tubelike cells inside the cortex carry food in the plant. These cells are called phloem cells. Label the phloem cells.

Data and Observations

Figure 1

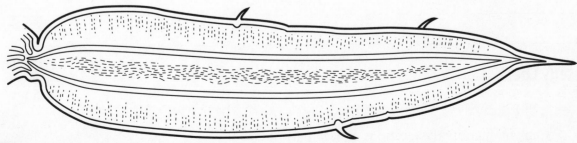

 SCI 5.a. Students know plants and animals have levels of organization for structure and function, including cells, tissues, organs, organ systems, and the whole organism.

Laboratory Activity 1 (continued)

Questions and Conclusions

1. What type of root is the carrot?

   _____

2. What is the function of the root hairs?

   _____

   _____

3. How many different kinds of cells did you see in the carrot slice?

   _____

4. What is the name and function of the outer ring of cells?

   _____

5. What is the green part at the top end of the carrot?

   _____

6. What is the name and function of the thicker layer of cells next to the epidermis?

   _____

7. What cells are found in the inner core?

   _____

8. What is the function of these cells?

   _____

   _____

9. Why do you think taproots are used as food more often than fibrous roots?

   _____

   _____

   _____

10. List some other food plants that have a taproot.

   _____

   _____

   _____

Strategy Check

_____ Can you examine a carrot root?

_____ Can you identify the locations of each part of a root?

Parts of a Fruit

Some of the plants we call vegetables are actually fruits. Fruits are formed inside flowers that have been pollinated and fertilized. After fertilization takes place, the petals fall off and the ovary begins to develop into the fruit.

Strategy

You will study the structure of typical fleshy and dry fruits.
You will examine several fruits and classify the fruits as fleshy or dry.

Materials

plum	peach	okra	pea in a pod	corn
tomato	peanut	olive	avocado	bean in a pod
apple	acorn	pear	sunflower seed	

Procedure

1. Read the following paragraphs and study the diagrams.

   The peach is a fleshy fruit. A fleshy fruit consists of a single ripened ovary with a soft, fleshy ovary wall when ripe. Three kinds of fleshy fruits are the drupe, pome, and the berry. The peach is a drupe. The exocarp is the covering or skin. The mesocarp is fleshy. The endocarp is hard and encloses the seed.

   The apple is a pome. The stem is the stalk by which the flower was attached. At the other end are the remains of the sepals, petals, and a ring of dried stamens. The thin skin is the epidermis. The fleshy part inside the skin developed from the receptacle, or flower stalk. The papery core is the ovary wall. Within the ovary are the seeds.

   The grape is a berry. The entire ovary is soft.

   Dry fruits have an ovary wall that is dry and brittle when ripe. They are classified as dehiscent or indehiscent. A dehiscent fruit splits along a definite seam when ripe. The bean is a dehiscent fruit called a legume. It splits along two seams.

2. Examine each of the fruits listed in Table 1 and determine if they are fleshy or dry. Determine the type of fruit (drupe, pome, or berry; dehiscent or indehiscent). Record your answers in the table.

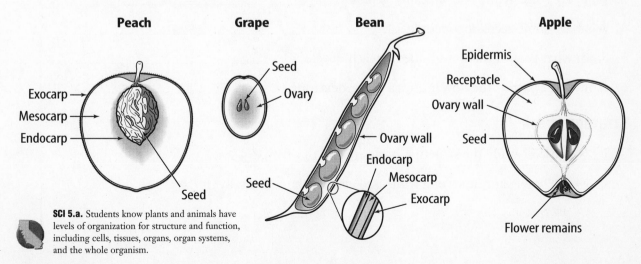

Peach — Exocarp, Mesocarp, Endocarp, Seed

Grape — Seed, Ovary

Bean — Seed, Ovary wall, Endocarp, Mesocarp, Exocarp

Apple — Epidermis, Receptacle, Ovary wall, Seed, Flower remains

SCI 5.a. Students know plants and animals have levels of organization for structure and function, including cells, tissues, organs, organ systems, and the whole organism.

Laboratory Activity 2 (continued)

Data and Observations

Table 1

Fruit	Fleshy or dry	Type
1. Plum		
2. Tomato		
3. Apple		
4. Peach		
5. Peanut		
6. Acorn		
7. Okra		
8. Olive		
9. Pear		
10. Pea		
11. Avocado		
12. Sunflower		
13. Corn		
14. Bean		

Questions and Conclusions

1. What part of a flower becomes the fruit? _____

2. What part of a flower becomes the seed? _____

3. What are some fruits that we call vegetables? _____

4. What are some seeds that people eat? _____

5. From what part of the flower does a peach develop? _____

6. From what part of the flower does a grape develop? _____

Strategy Check

_____ Did you study the structure of fleshy and dry fruits?

_____ Did you examine several fruits and classify them as fleshy or dry?

LAB

1 Laboratory Activity

Parts of a Seed

Seeds are important to plants because they aid in reproduction. When a seed is opened, you can usually find a miniature plant (embryo) inside that is surrounded by a food supply. If planted, the embryo grows into a new plant. Some seeds can be easily split into equal halves or cotyledons (the stored food), while others cannot be split. Those seeds that can be split evenly are called dicotyledons (*di* means two), while those that cannot be split are called monocotyledons (*mono* means one).

Strategy

You will observe and identify the parts of a lima bean seed.
You will learn the functions of seed parts.
You will examine and compare other seeds with a lima bean.
You will learn the difference between a monocotyledon and a dicotyledon seed.

Materials

scalpel
seeds (each soaked in water for 24 hours)
    lima bean
    peanut
    corn
    sunflower
    pea
WARNING: *Use care when handling sharp objects. Some kinds of seeds are poisonous. Do not place any seeds in your mouth.*

Procedure

1. Use your fingernail to carefully peel off the thin outer covering or seed coat from a soaked lima bean. Split the seed in half and identify the parts shown in Figure 1.
2. Remove the seed coat from the following soaked seeds: peanut, corn, sunflower, pea. Split each seed in half. Those seeds that do not open easily after the seed coat is removed should be sliced open lengthwise using a scalpel. **WARNING:** *Use care when cutting with a scalpel to avoid injury to yourself and others.*
3. Identify the seed parts.

Figure 1

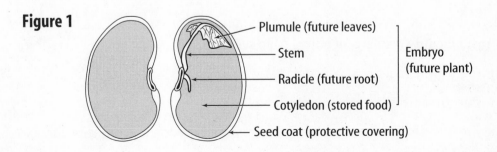

Plumule (future leaves)
Stem
Radicle (future root)
Cotyledon (stored food)
Seed coat (protective covering)
Embryo (future plant)

SCI 2.a. Students know the differences between the life cycles and reproduction methods of sexual and asexual organisms.

Laboratory Activity 1 (continued)

Data and Observations

Table 1

			Seed Structure		
Type of seed	Seed coat (hard or soft)	Easily opened cotyledons (yes or no)	Number of cotyledons (one or two)	Seed category (monocotyledon or dicotyledon)	Plumule and radicle (yes or no)
1. Lima bean					
2. Peanut					
3. Corn					
4. Sunflower					
5. Pea					

Questions and Conclusions

1. What is the function of the seed coat and the cotyledons?

   _____

2. Why is it important that all seeds have a supply of stored food?

   _____

3. How does the ease of splitting open a monocotyledon seed compare with that of splitting open a dicotyledon seed?

   _____

4. Were there any seeds without a plumule and radicle?

   _____

5. What would you expect to grow if a seed without a plumule and radicle were planted?

   _____

Strategy Check

_____ Can you identify the parts of a lima bean seed?

_____ Can you list the functions of seed parts?

_____ Can you compare other seeds with a lima bean?

_____ Can you identify the difference between a monocotyledon and a dicotyledon seed?

LAB 2 Laboratory Activity

Examining Models of Chromosomes

Models of the chromosomes of the imaginary Leksak bird can be found at the end of this lab. The dark bands on these chromosome models are genes. Most cells in this bird's body contain the same number and type of chromosomes. The importance of genes to all living things, and to the Leksak bird as well, is that they control all inherited traits. Chromosomes are important because they are the carriers of these genes.

Strategy

You will cut out and pair chromosome models of the Leksak bird.
You will determine what type of change occurs in the number of chromosomes when a cell divides by mitosis and meiosis.

Materials

scissors

Procedure/Data and Observations

1. Cut out each chromosome model in Figure 1.
2. Fold each paper model in half along dotted lines.
3. Match in pairs as many chromosome models as possible. A chromosome pair must match in length as well as in number and location of genes. The lines on the chromosome models represent genes.
4. Answer questions 1 through 4 in Questions and Conclusions before proceeding further.
5. Cut each chromosome model in half along the dotted line. Make two piles of chromosome halves. Put one half of each chromosome in one pile and the other half in the second pile.
6. Compare the chromosomes in the first pile with those in the second pile.

Cell division includes a process called mitosis that occurs in most living things. During mitosis, a cell's nucleus divides into two nuclei. The cutting of each chromosome model and separating them into two piles is similar to what happens in a living cell during cell division. The two piles of chromosome models represent two new cells. (Each chromosome duplicates itself and the two halves then separate.)

7. Before proceeding, answer questions 5 and 6 in Questions and Conclusions.
8. Place all identical chromosome models together in separate groups. You should have six groups of models.
9. Take a group of matched chromosomes and separate them into four piles. Take a second group of matched chromosomes and place one chromosome from the group into each of the four piles.
10. Continue this sorting until all chromosome models, including the unmatched chromosome models, have been separated into the four piles. Each pile of chromosome models represents a sex cell.

A process called meiosis occurs in some living things. During meiosis, a cell's nucleus divides twice so that one diploid cell divides to produce four haploid cells. Each new cell produced by this process is called a sex cell (egg or sperm).

SCI 2.b. Students know sexual reproduction produces offspring that inherit half their genes from each parent.

Laboratory Activity 2 (continued)

Questions and Conclusions

1. How many chromosomes can be found in each of the Leksak bird's cells?

_____

2. How many matched pairs of chromosomes are there in each cell?

_____

3. How many unmatched chromosomes are there in each cell?

_____

4. Do the genes on each matched pair of chromosomes also match?

_____

5. After separating the chromosome model halves into two piles, how many models are found in each pile?

_____

6. How many chromosomes are found in Leksak sex cells?

_____

7. Do any chromosomes match one another in a sex cell?

_____

8. Male Leksak birds have six matched pairs of chromosomes and one unmatched pair of chromosomes. Female Leksak birds have seven matched pairs of chromosomes. Were the chromosomes in our bird taken from a male or a female?

_____

9. Are all cells produced by mitosis exactly alike, chromosome for chromosome? Gene for gene? Explain why.

_____

_____

10. How does the number of chromosomes in sex cells compare to the number of chromosomes in cells formed during mitosis?

_____

_____

11. Explain two ways in which sex cells differ from all other cells.

_____

Strategy Check

_____ Did you cut out and match in pairs the chromosome models of the Leksak bird?

_____ Did you determine the types of changes that occur in the number of chromosomes when a cell undergoes mitosis or meiosis?

Laboratory Activity 2 (continued)

Figure 1

Models of chromosomes for the imaginary Leksak bird after duplication in the interphase period of the cell cycle.

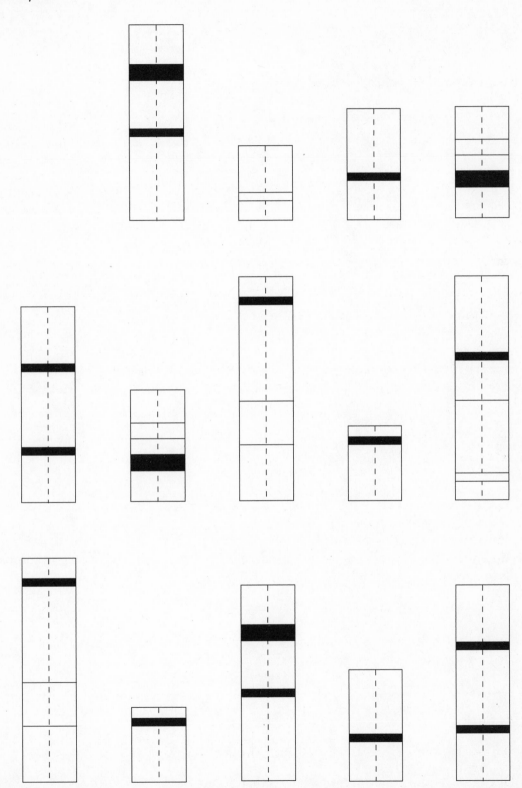

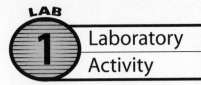

Genetic Traits

SCI 2.c. Students know an inherited trait can be determined by one or more genes.

Have you ever been told you look like your parents? Parents pass genes that determine physical features to their children. These physical features are called genetic traits. Children receive half of their genes from each parent. The genes of one parent may be dominant over the genes of the other parent. A child usually looks most like the parent who supplies the most dominant genes.

Strategy
You will examine some of your genetic traits.
You will examine your parents for the same genetic traits.
You will compare how similar or different you and your parents are.

Materials
pencil

Procedure
1. Work with a partner during this activity. Complete the column marked "You" in Table 1 in Data and Observations for each of the genetic traits listed. Ask your partner to help you describe the traits you cannot see. Refer to Figure 1 for an explanation of traits you may not be familiar with.
2. Optional: Take the table home and complete it for each of your parents.

Figure 1

Hair Whorl

Ear Lobe

Clockwise   Counterclockwise   Free   Attached

Cheek

Tongue

Dimples   No dimples   Nonroller   Roller

Laboratory Activity 1 (continued)

Data and Observations

Record your results in the table.

Table 1

Trait	Description	You	Father	Mother
Handedness	Left or right			
Sight	Nearsighted or normal			
Eye color	Blue or not blue			
Dimples*	Yes or no			
Freckles	Present or absent			
Hair whorl*	Clockwise or counterclockwise			
Earlobe*	Free or attached			
Tongue*	Roller or nonroller			

* See Figure 1.

Questions and Conclusions

1. How many traits do you and your mother share?

   _____

   You and your father?

   _____

2. How many traits do you share with both parents?

   _____

3. List all traits that you show but are not shown by either parent.

   _____

4. How might it be possible to show a trait when both parents do not show it?

   _____

5. What proof do you have that all of your genes did not come from only one parent?

   _____

Strategy Check

_____ Can you identify some genetic traits?

_____ Can you count how many traits are the same for each parent and you?

_____ Can you make any conclusions about the traits you received from each parent?

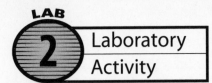

50:50 Chances

LAB 2 Laboratory Activity

The chance of a flipped coin landing with the "heads" side up rather than the "tails" side is 50:50. Does that mean that for every two times a coin is flipped, heads will turn up once and tails will turn up once? The chance of a boy rather than a girl being born in a family is also 50:50. Does that mean that in a family with six children, three are boys and three are girls? You know the answer to both of these questions is no. What is the value, then, of saying the chances are 50:50?

Strategy

You will compare the chances of a boy or girl being born with the chances of a flipped coin landing on one side or the other.

You will flip a coin six times to represent the sexes of children in one family.

You will record your results and compare the sexes of the children in 15 families.

Materities

Materials
coin

Procedure

1. Let the heads side of the coin represent girls. Let the tails side represent boys. Flip the coin six times. How many times did girls turn up? How many times did boys turn up? Record these totals in Table 1 under Group 1.

2. Continue to flip the coin until you have a total of 15 groups of six flips each.

Data and Observations

Table 1

Group	1	2	3	4	5	6	7	8	9	10	11	12	13	14	15
Girls (heads)															
Boys (tails)															

1. Use slash marks **/** to complete Table 2 using the data recorded in Table 1 for each group of six flips.

SCI 2.c. Students know an inherited trait can be determined by one or more genes. Also covers **SCI 2.d.**

Laboratory Activity 2 (continued)

Table 2

Possible combinations	6 girls 0 boys	5 girls 1 boy	4 girls 2 boys	3 girls 3 boys	2 girls 4 boys	1 girl 5 boys	0 girls 6 boys
Number of combinations							

Questions and Conclusions

1. Why can you use coin flips to represent sex combinations that may occur in families?

_____

2. According to your results, is it possible to have a family of exactly three boys and three girls?

_____

Do you know any family where there are exactly three boys and three girls?

_____

3. According to your results, is it possible to have a family of six children where the ratio of boys to girls is not exactly 50:50?_____

Do you know of actual families where this is true?_____

4. According to your results, which combination of boys and girls occurred the most often?

_____

Does this agree with what you had expected?_____

5. Explain how one can make a statement that you expect three boys and three girls in every family of six children, but yet you may not get this ratio in an actual family.

_____

6. Out of 90 total children (flips) counted, how many were males?_____ Females?_____

Is your answer close to half boys and half girls?_____ Explain

_____

7. In a single family, the ratio may or may not be half boys and half girls. When do you begin to show that an equal number of boys and girls occurs in families?

_____

Strategy Check

_____ Can you compare the chance of a boy or girl being born with the chance of a coin landing on one side or the other?

_____ Can you compare the sexes of the children in 15 families by flipping a coin?

_____ Can you explain how numbers, such as 50:50, can be used to show the likelihood of an occurrence?

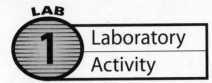

Differences in a Species

SCI 3.a. Students know both genetic variation and environmental factors are causes of evolution and diversity of organisms.

To use fossil dating efficiently, paleontologists first separate fossils into groups. The most useful group for classification is called a species. A species is a population of individuals that have similar characteristics. Small differences in individuals might result in the development of a new species by a series of gradual changes. These changes can be traced from one geologic time division to another if the fossil record is good.

Strategy

You will describe the variations present within a species.
You will describe a species in terms of one characteristic.

Materials

meterstick   graph paper   pencils (colored)

Procedure

1. The species you will study is *Homo sapiens,* or yourself. You and your classmates are all members of this species. Remember that all living things grow at different rates. It is possible that you will find some big differences in your study, but everyone still belongs to the same species.

2. Record all characteristics of the species that you can. Record which of the characteristics you could measure and compare for all members of the species.

3. Measure and record in Table 1 the height of yourself and each of your classmates. Round off the height to the nearest tenth of a meter (0.1 m).

4. Measure the heights of a class of younger students. Record this data in Table 2.

Data and Observations

1. Characteristics: _____

_____

Table 1

Name	Height (m)	Name	Height (m)	Name	Height (m)

Laboratory Activity 1 (continued)

Table 2

Name	Height (m)	Name	Height (m)	Name	Height (m)

Use a separate sheet of paper to graph the Frequency (number of persons having the same height) on the vertical axis against the Height (m) on the horizontal axis. Use one color for your own class and a second color for the younger class.

Questions and Conclusions

1. On what characteristics can you classify this group as a single species?

_____

2. Where do most of the members of your class fall in regard to height?

_____

3. Where do most of the members of the younger class fall in regard to height?

_____

4. What change has taken place over time?

_____

5. How is this activity like fossil dating?

_____

_____

6. How is this activity different from fossil dating? (Hint: Think in terms of the time spans involved.)

_____

_____

Strategy Check

_____ Can you describe the variations present within a species?

_____ Can you describe a species in terms of a range of a characteristic?

Copyright © Glencoe/McGraw-Hill, a division of The McGraw-Hill Companies, Inc.

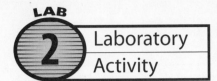

Bird Beaks and Physical Adaptations

Birds are common in every part of the country. Have you ever looked at a bird's beak and wondered why it is it shaped the way it is? Many animals have physical adaptations that help them in obtaining food. This activity explores the shapes of bird beaks and how the beaks are adapted to different food sources.

Strategy

You will infer that birds have physically adapted in relation to the type of food supply. You will deduce what beaks are most efficient for specific types of food.

Materials

Group 1: colored water in 10 mL graduated cylinder, shoestring, dropper, sponge strip
Group 2: gummy worms in potting soil, straw, chopsticks, wrench
Group 3: sunflower seeds in shallow pan, pliers, chopsticks, tweezers
Group 4: styrofoam squares in dish of water, pliers, chopsticks, tweezers
Group 5: loose tea in dish of water, slotted spoon, strainer, tweezers
Group 6: popped popcorn, tongs, envelope, chopsticks
Group 7: rice in tree bark, dropper, tongs, tweezers
Group 8: marshmallows hanging on strings, chopsticks, tongs, turkey skewer
All groups: cup, graph paper

Procedure

1. Find your group number in Table 1. Assemble your food source and sample beaks.

2. Read the description of the challenge and any additional information listed in Table 1 to help you understand your challenge. Examine the beaks. Note the type of food source in the space provided in the Data and Observations section. Write the type of beaks that your group is using in Table 2. Decide who in the group will perform the challenge with each sample beak and who will keep time.

3. As a group, perform the challenge at least three times with each sample beak. Record the time in seconds for each trial in Table 2 in the Data and Observations section.

4. Calculate the average time for each beak. Enter this information in Table 2.

5. On a piece of graph paper, construct a bar graph showing the average time for each sample beak.

6. Examine the graphs describing the average time for each beak type and food source from all of the groups. Use the average times to determine the most efficient beak type for each food source. Enter your selection in Table 3 in the Data and Observations section.

7. In the last column of Table 3, sketch a bird beak that resembles the instrument you used as a sample beak.

Copyright © Glencoe/McGraw-Hill, a division of The McGraw-Hill Companies, Inc.

 SCI 3.a. Students know both genetic variation and environmental factors are causes of evolution and diversity of organisms. Also covers **SCI 3.c.**

Laboratory Activity 2 (continued)

Data and Observations

Table 1

Group	Food source	Sample beaks	Challenge	Additional instructions
1	graduated cylinder	shoestring dropper sponge strip	Transfer 10 mL of water from a graduated cylinder to a cup.	
2	gummy worms	straw chopsticks wrench	Remove gummy from dirt.	Bury the worms after each trial.
3	sunflower seeds	pliers chopsticks tweezers	Crack the shell and remove the seed inside.	
4	floating plastic foam squares	chopsticks tweezers slotted spoon	Remove all of the plastic foam from the water.	Return the squares after each trial.
5	tea	slotted spoon strainer tweezers	Remove all of the tea from the water.	Return the tea after each trial.
6	popped corn	tongs envelope chopsticks	Capture 20 kernels.	A partner tosses some kernels into the air. You must catch the kernels while they are still in the air.
7	rice	dropper tongs tweezers	Remove 30 grains of rice from the bark of a tree.	
8	marshmallows hanging from a string	chopsticks tongs turkey skewer	Remove 5 marshmallows from the strings.	

Table 2

	Time (s)			
Type of Beak	Trial 1	Trial 2	Trial 3	Average
1.				
2.				
3.				

Laboratory Activity 2 (continued)

Table 3

Food Source	Most efficient beak type	Sketch
Water in graduated cylinder		
Gummy worms in soil		
Sunflower seeds in shallow pan		
Floating cubes of plastic foam		
Loose tea in water		
Popped popcorn in air		
Rice in tree bark		
Marshmallows on string		

Laboratory Activity 2 (continued)

Questions and Conclusions

1. What are animal adaptations?

_____

2. Explain why birds have different shaped beaks.

_____

3. What happens if an environment is altered?

_____

4. Why can birds with different beak types share a habitat?

_____

Directions: *Write the letter of the food source and type of bird described in Column II in the space beside the lab set-up described in Column I.*

Column I

_____ 5. colored water in a tall, thin vase

_____ 6. gummy worms buried in potting soil

_____ 7. sunflower seeds spread in a pan

_____ 8. plastic foam cubes floating in shallow water

_____ 9. loose-leaf tea or herbs in a dish of water

_____ 10. popped popcorn

_____ 11. rice grains tucked into the bark of a log

_____ 12. marshmallows hanging on strings

Column II

a. nectar sucked out of flowers (hummingbird)

b. fish scooped out of water (heron)

c. flying insects caught in wide openings (swallow)

d. worms dug and pulled out of soil (robin)

e. meat pulled off bones (owl, hawk)

f. seeds cracked open (sparrow, finch)

g. small insects picked and pried out of small crevices (woodpecker)

h. fine bits of vegetation carefully scooped out of water (duck, goose, swan)

Strategy Check

_____ Can you predict what a bird's food source is based on the shape of its beak?

_____ Can you determine which beak type is most efficient for a given food source?

Classification

If you were asked to classify objects, you would probably group together those objects that have a certain characteristic in common. A scientist does the same thing when grouping or classifying living things. Living things are grouped according to certain likenesses or similar characteristics. Each group may then be divided into subgroups. Each group and subgroup is given a name to help simplify the scientist's work.

Strategy

You will classify paper shapes.
You will use the words *kingdom*, *phylum*, and *class* in your classifying system.
You will determine what characteristics you are using to make your classification.

Materials

paper (2 sheets)
scissors

Procedure

1. Cut out the 13 shapes shown in Figure 1. **WARNING**: *Always be careful when using scissors.*

2. Place shapes 3, 4, 6, 7, 9, 10, and 11 into one group. This will represent the first kingdom. Place these shapes on a separate piece of notebook paper.

3. Place shapes 1, 2, 5, 8, 12, and 13 into a second group, or second kingdom. Place these shapes on a separate piece of notebook paper.

4. Keep the kingdom shapes on the same paper. Further separate them into smaller

groups. Place shapes 3, 4, 7, and 10 into one group. This will represent the first phylum.

5. Place shapes 6 and 9 into another group. This will be the second phylum.

6. Place shape 11 by itself for the third phylum.

7. The phyla may be further subdivided by writing an identification letter on each one. Each subgroup will represent a class. On shapes 3, 4, and 7 write the letter A.

8. On shape 10 write the letter B.

Questions and Conclusions

1. How do members of the first kingdom differ from the members of the second kingdom?

_____

_____

_____

2. What two names would you suggest to describe the characteristics common to the two kingdoms?

_____

_____

_____

SCI 3.d. Students know how to construct a simple branching diagram to classify living groups of organisms by shared derived characteristics and how to expand the diagram to include fossil organisms.

Laboratory Activity 1 (continued)

3. What characteristics do shapes 3, 4, 7, and 10 have that make them different from 6, 9, or 11?

_____

_____

4. How are 6 and 9 different from 11?

_____

_____

5. If you had to use a name to describe the characteristics common to members of the first phylum, what would be a suitable name?

_____

_____

What name would best describe the second phylum?

_____

_____

The third phylum?

_____

_____

6. On the class level, what characteristics do shapes 3, 4, and 7 have that make them different from 10?

_____

_____

7. What would best describe the class for shapes 3, 4, and 7?

_____

_____

For 10?

_____

Strategy Check

_____ Can you classify paper shapes into large and smaller groups based on similar characteristics?

_____ Can you name the groups using descriptive terms?

Laboratory Activity 1 (continued)

Figure 1

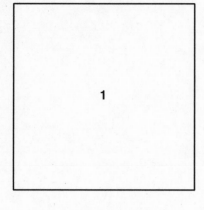

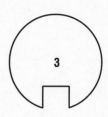

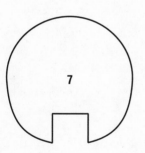

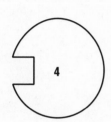

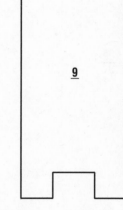

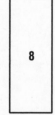

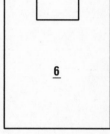

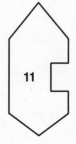

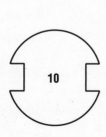

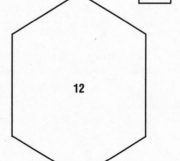

LAB 2 — Laboratory Activity

Seed Adaptations

An adaptation is any variation that makes an organism better suited to its environment. Adaptations are evident in all living things, including plants.

Strategy

You will determine if water temperature affects seed germination.
You will determine if scraping seed coats affects seed germination.
You will explain how seed adaptations may help plants survive and reproduce.

Materials

hot plate   paper towels
water   plastic lunch bags
small beakers   masking tape and pen
honey locust seeds   coarse sandpaper

Procedure

Part A—Seed Coat and Water Temperature

1. Using a hot plate, heat a small amount of water in a beaker until it is boiling. **WARNING:** *Do not touch beaker with unprotected hands. Glass, water, and plate are hot.* Put the same amount of cold water into a second beaker.

2. Place ten honey locust seeds in each beaker as shown in Figure 1.

3. After 15 min, remove all seeds from the beakers. Wrap each group of seeds in a separate paper towel.

4. Moisten each towel and place it in a sealable plastic bag. Use Figure 2 as a guide.

5. Label each bag with your name, the date, and either "hot" or "cold" depending on which beaker the seeds were in.

6. Set the bags aside for 48 h.

Part B—Seed Coat and Scraping

1. Place ten honey locust seeds between wet paper towels. Place the towels and seeds in a plastic bag.

2. Label this bag with your name, the date, and "unscraped."

Figure 1

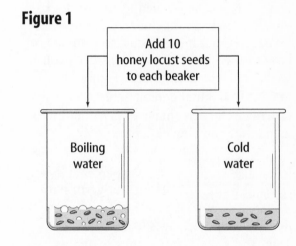

Add 10 honey locust seeds to each beaker

Boiling water   Cold water

Figure 2

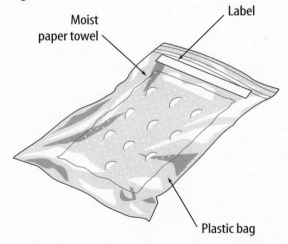

Moist paper towel

Label

Plastic bag

SCI 3.a. Students know both genetic variation and environmental factors are causes of evolution and diversity of organisms.

Laboratory Activity 2 (continued)

3. Prepare ten scraped honey locust seeds. While holding a honey locust seed tightly between your fingers, rub the same spot of the seed across the surface of a piece of coarse sandpaper. Press hard and rub each seed exactly ten times. Use Figure 3 as a guide.
4. Place these seeds between wet paper towels. Place the towels and seeds in a plastic bag.
5. Label the bag with your name, the date, and "scraped."
6. Set the bags aside for 48 h.

Part C—Accumulation of Data

1. After 48 h, open each seed bag and count the number of seeds that have germinated. A seed has germinated if there is a root extending from the seed. However, seeds about to germinate will be swollen to almost double their original volume due to the water intake. Because honey locust seeds may not have formed roots in 48 h, consider swollen seeds as having germinated (Figure 4).
2. Record individual data in Table 1.
3. Calculate the percentage of germination by using the following equation.

$$\frac{\text{number of germinated seeds}}{\text{total number of seeds}} \times 100 = \frac{\text{percentage of germination}}{}$$

4. Record the percentages in Table 1.
5. Total and record class results in Table 2.

Figure 3

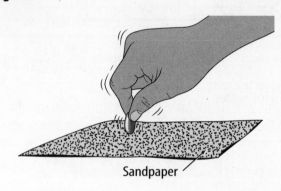

Sandpaper

Figure 4

Honey locust seeds
(natural size)

Nongerminated

Germinated

Data and Observations

Table 1

Numbers and Percentages of Germinated Seeds—Individual Results			
	Number of seeds used	Number that germinated	Percentage of germination
Hot water			
Cold water			
Scraped			
Unscraped			

Laboratory Activity 2 (continued)

Table 2

Numbers and Percentages of Germinated Seeds—Class Results			
	Number of seeds used	Number that germinated	Percentage of germination
Hot water			
Cold water			
Scraped			
Unscraped			

Questions and Conclusions

1. A seed coat serves as a barrier to germination. Water must penetrate this barrier for the seed to germinate.
   a. Does the hard coat of honey locust seeds block or allow cold water to pass through? (Use class results from Table 2.)

   _____

   b. Does the hard coat of honey locust seeds block or allow hot water to pass through? (Use class results from Table 2.)

   _____

   c. At which temperature is water better able to pass through the seed coat?

   _____

2. Honey locust seeds are formed in the late fall. The seeds may fall to the ground in the early winter.

   a. Would the water temperature in soil in early winter be warm or cold? _____

   b. Could water easily pass through the seed coat of honey locusts at this time? _____

   c. Will honey locust seeds start to germinate at this time? _____

   d. Would young honey locust trees have a good chance of survival if they started growing in

   the winter? _____

3. Honey locust seeds remain in the soil until the following spring or summer.

   a. Would the water temperatures in soil during spring or summer be warmer or colder than

   in winter? _____

   b. Could water more easily pass through the seed coat of honey locusts at this time?

   _____

   c. Would young honey locust trees have a good chance of survival if they started growing in

   the spring? _____

Copyright © Glencoe/McGraw-Hill, a division of The McGraw-Hill Companies, Inc.

Laboratory Activity 2 (continued)

4. Seed responses to water temperature are inherited genetic traits. Seeds that germinate in nature during cold weather will not survive. Seeds that germinate in nature during warm weather will have a better chance of surviving. This ability to germinate only in warm weather is called an adaptation.

   a. Which seeds are more likely to survive, those that germinate in cold or warm weather?

   _____

   b. Which seeds are less likely to survive?

   _____

   c. Which trait is more likely to be passed on to future generations?

   _____

5. Does the scraped seed coat of honey locust seeds block water or allow it to pass through?

   (Use class results from Table 2.) _____

6. **a.** Assuming that honey locust seeds fall to the ground in late fall or early winter, other than water temperature, what factor seems to prevent early seed germination?

   _____

   b. Could the seed coat barrier to germination be a helpful variation? _____

7. Suggest a possible way that the seed coat of a honey locust might be "scraped" in nature.

   _____

8. Name the two honey locust seed adaptations that were studied in Part A and Part B of this experiment.

   _____

9. **a.** Do adaptations make survival easier or more difficult for organisms? _____

   b. Define the term *adaptation.* _____

   _____

10. Why are class data rather than individual data used to draw conclusions?

   _____

11. Describe an adaptation shown by

   a. climbing vines _____

   b. cactus plants _____

Strategy Check

_____ Can you determine if water temperature affects seed germination?

_____ Can you determine if scraping seed coats affects seed germination?

_____ Can you explain how seed adaptations may help plants survive and reproduce?

Principle of Superposition

SCI 4.c. Students know that the rock cycle includes the formation of new sediment and rocks and that rocks are often found in layers, with the oldest generally on the bottom. Also covers **SCI 4.a.**

The principle of superposition states that beds in a series are laid down with the oldest at the bottom and successively younger layers on top. Beds may be exposed at the surface as a result of folding and uplifting or because of faulting. If part, or all, of a layer is removed by erosion and this surface is covered by a new deposit, the contact is called an unconformity. In some areas, river erosion will cut deeply enough to expose a number of layers, such as in the Grand Canyon.

Strategy

You will construct a map legend.
You will construct a block diagram of an area.
You will write the geologic history of the area.

Materials

block diagram, Figure 1
glue or paste
cardboard, thin
pencils (colored)
scissors
tape (clear)

Procedure

1. Set up a legend for your diagram and select a color for each layer. Record the legend in Table 1.
2. Glue Figure 1 on the cardboard. Color the map according to your legend.
3. Cut out, fold, and tape the block diagram as instructed on Figure 1.

Data and Observations

Table 1

	Color
Layer A	
Layer B	
Layer C	
Layer D	

Questions and Conclusions

1. Which layer is oldest? Explain.

_____

_____

_____

2. What kind of structure do the layers have?

_____

_____

Laboratory Activity 1 (continued)

3. Why is the glacial till not folded?

_____

_____

_____

4. What does the presence of the peat and soil layer in the glacial till tell you?

_____

_____

_____

5. Was this a mountainous area prior to glaciation? Explain.

_____

_____

_____

_____

_____

6. How many advances of the ice occurred here?

_____

7. Write the geologic history of the area illustrated in the block diagram.

_____

_____

_____

_____

_____

_____

_____

_____

Strategy Check

_____ Can you set up a map legend?

_____ Can you construct a block diagram?

_____ Can you write the geologic history of the area illustrated by a block diagram?

Laboratory Activity 1 (continued)

Figure 1

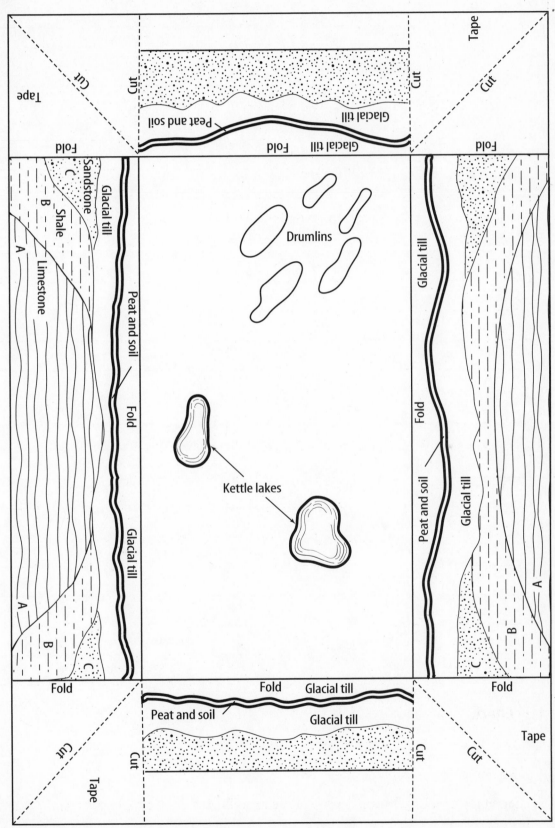

LAB 2 Laboratory Activity

Radioactive Decay— A Simulation

Certain elements are made up of atoms whose nuclei are naturally unstable. The atoms of these elements are said to be radioactive. The nucleus of a radioactive atom will decay into the nucleus of another element by emitting particles of radiation. It is impossible to predict when the nucleus of an individual radioactive atom will decay. However, if a large number of nuclei are present in a sample, it is possible to predict the time period in which half the nuclei in the sample will decay. This time period is called the half-life of the element.

Radioactive materials are harmful to living tissues. Their half-lives are difficult to measure without taking safety precautions. To eliminate these problems, you will simulate the decay of unstable nuclei by using harmless materials that are easy to observe. In this experiment you will use dried split peas to represent the unstable nuclei of one element. Dried lima beans will represent the stable nuclei of another element. Your observations will allow you to make a mental model of how the nuclei of radioactive atoms decay.

Strategy

You will simulate the decay of a radioactive element.
You will graph the results of the simulated decay.
You will determine the half-life of the element.

Materials

small bag of dried split peas
250-mL beaker
large pizza or baking tray
bag of dried lima beans

Procedure

1. Count out 200 dried split peas and place them in a beaker.
2. Record the number of split peas in Table 1 as Observation 0.
3. Place the pizza or baking tray on a flat surface.
4. Hold the beaker over the tray and sprinkle the split peas onto the tray. Try to produce a single layer of split peas on the tray.
5. Remove all the split peas that have NOT landed on the flat side down. Count the split peas that you have removed and return them to the bag. Replace the number of peas that you have removed from the tray with an equal number of lima beans. Count the number of peas and the number of lima beans on the tray. Record these values in Table 1 as Observation 1.

6. Scoop the peas and beans from the tray and place them into the beaker.
7. Predict how many split peas you will remove if you repeat steps 4 and 5. Enter your predictions in the Data and Observations section.
8. Repeat steps 4 through 6, recording your data in the data table as Observation 2.
9. Predict how many observations you will have to make until there are no split peas remaining. Enter your prediction in the Data and Observations section.
10. Repeat steps 4 through 6 until there are no split peas remaining.

SCI 4.d. Students know that evidence from geologic layers and radioactive dating indicates Earth is approximately 4.6 billion years old and that life on this planet has existed for more than 3 billion years.

Laboratory Activity 2 (continued)

Data and Observations

Table 1

Observation	Time (minutes)	Split peas	Lima beans

Prediction of number of split peas removed:

_____

Prediction of number of observations until there are no split peas remaining:

_____

Laboratory Activity 2 (continued)

Analysis

In this experiment each split pea represents the nucleus of an atom of radioactive element A. A split pea that has landed flat side down represents the nucleus of an atom of radioactive element A that has not yet decayed. Each split pea that has NOT landed flat side down represents the nucleus of element A that has decayed. Each lima bean represents the nucleus of an element B that was formed by the decay of the nucleus of an element A .

Assume that the time period between each observation was 5 minutes. Observation 1 will have been made at 5 minutes, observation 2 at 10 minutes, and so on. Complete the time column in Table 1.

1. Use Graph 1 below to graph the results of your experiment. Plot on one axis the number of the nuclei of element A atoms remaining after each observation. Plot the time of this observation on the other axis. Determine which variable should be represented by each axis.

2. Use Graph 1 to construct another graph. Plot on one axis the number of nuclei of element B atoms remaining after each observation. Plot the time of the observation on the other axis.

3. Determine the appropriate half-life of element A from your graph.

Graph 1

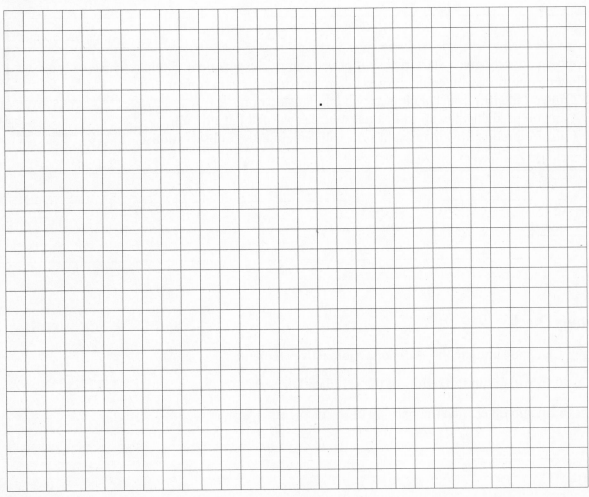

Laboratory Activity 2 (continued)

Questions and Conclusions

1. What is the approximate half-life of element A?

_____

2. Use your graph to determine the number of element A nuclei remaining after 2 half-lives, and after 3 half-lives.

_____

3. Why did you replace split peas but not lima beans during this experiment?

_____

_____

_____

4. The two graphs that you constructed look like mirror-images. Explain why this is so.

_____

_____

_____

5. Suppose you were given 400 dried split peas to do this experiment. Explain which of the following questions you could answer before starting this experiment.
  a. Can you identify which split peas will fall flat side up?
  b. Can you predict when an individual split pea will fall flat side up?
  c. Can you predict how many split peas will remain after 3 observations?

_____

_____

_____

_____

_____

Strategy Check

_____ Can you simulate the decay of a radioactive element?

_____ Can you graph the results of the simulated decay?

_____ Can you determine the half-life of the element?

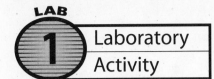

Looking at the Geologic Time Scale

SCI 4.g. Students know how to explain significant developments and extinctions of plant and animal life on the geologic time scale. Also covers **SCI 4.d.**

As you have learned, Earth's history can be divided in geologic time segments called eras, periods, and epochs. These time periods are useful for placing events such as the disappearance of the dinosaurs and the appearance of humans in perspective relative to the history of life on Earth. The time segments are not as equal as they sound, however. In earlier eras, life processes on Earth appear to have been developing quite slowly, whereas later eras saw enormous changes over relatively short segments of geologic time. In this Laboratory Activity you will compare and contrast various segments of Earth's history by constructing a geologic time line.

Strategy

You will make a graph to compare the durations of Earth's geologic eras.
You will measure and construct a time line that shows Earth's geologic eras.
You will identify time relationships among events in Earth's geologic history.
You will record and illustrate significant events during the Mesozoic and Cenozoic Eras on a time line.

Materials

4–4.5 m of adding machine tape
meter stick
colored pencils

Procedure

Part A

1. Figure 1 shows approximately how long ago each major division of Earth's geologic time scale began. Use the information to calculate how long each of these divisions lasted. Record that information in the last column of Figure 1.
2. Using that information, make a bar graph on the grid in the Data and Observations section to show how long each division lasted.

Part B

3. You will use a piece of adding machine tape to make a geologic time line. Distance will represent time, with 1 cm representing 10 million years.
4. Using the meter stick, draw a straight line through the middle of the tape from one end to the other.
5. Starting at the left end of the tape, measure a distance that represents the length of Precambrian Time. Refer back to the time duration you calculated in Figure 1. Make a vertical line at the correct point.

To the left of that line label the division on your time line *Precambrian Time.*
6. From that vertical line, measure a distance that represents the length of the Paleozoic Era. Refer back to the time duration you calculated in Figure 1. Make a vertical line at the correct point. To the left of that line, label the division on your time line *Paleozoic Era.*
7. Repeat step 6 for the Mesozoic Era and the Cenozoic Era.
8. Lightly color each division on your time line a different color.
9. Divide the Mesozoic Era and the Cenozoic Era into the Periods and Epochs shown in Figure 2.
10. Then, using information from your text (such as the mass extinction) and the additional information in Figure 2, mark in the correct positions on your time line for significant events that occurred during the Mesozoic and Paleozoic Eras. Illustrate each of these events with a small drawing.

Laboratory Activity 1 (continued)

Data and Observations

Figure 1

Major geologic time division	When time division began	Length of time division lasted
Precambrian time	4.0 billion years ago	
Paleozoic era	544 million years ago	
Mesozoic era	245 million years ago	
Cenozoic era	65 million years ago	

Figure 2

Division	Time period (millions of years ago)	Event(s)
Triassic period	248–213	breakup of Pangaea
Jurassic period	213–145	first birds
Cretaceous period	145–65	Rocky Mountains form; first flowering plants
Paleocene epoch	65–55.5	first hooved mammals
Eocene epoch	55.5–33.7	first whales
Oligocene epoch	33.7–23.8	early formation of European Alps
Miocene epoch	23.8–5.3	first dogs and bears
Pliocene epoch	5.3–1.8	first Ice Age; first hominoids
Pleistocene epoch	1.8–0.008	modern humans
Holocene epoch	0.0008–present	Sea levels rose as climate warmed; first civilizations

Laboratory Activity 1 (continued)

Graph

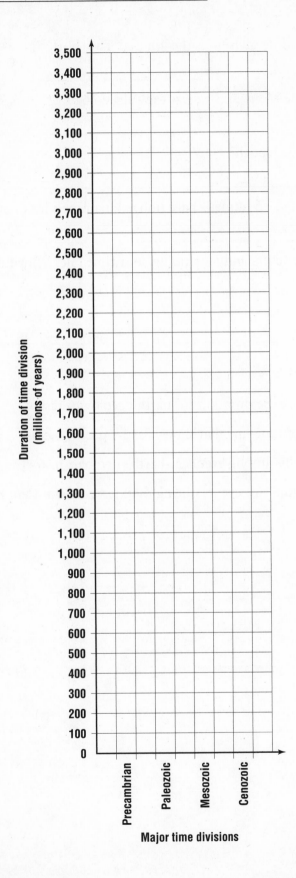

Laboratory Activity 1 (continued)

Questions and Conclusions

1. Based on your graph in Part A, which time division is the longest? The shortest?

_____

2. About how many times longer than the Mesozoic Era was the Paleozoic Era?

_____

3. In which era do you live today? In which epoch?

_____

4. About how many times longer than modern humans have hooved mammals lived on Earth?

_____

5. What problems did you have in constructing and illustrating your time line? Why did you have those problems?

_____

_____

Strategy Check

_____ Can you make a graph to compare the durations of Earth's geologic eras?

_____ Can you measure and construct a time line that shows Earth's geologic eras?

_____ Can you identify time relationships among events in Earth's geologic history?

_____ Can you record and illustrate significant events during the Mesozoic and Cenozoic Eras on a time line?

Modeling Geographic Isolation

The traits of a species can change over time. Individuals moving into or out of an area can add variation to the genetic makeup of a species in a particular area. When a small part of a population is isolated, they will usually have fewer variations of traits than exist in a large population. You can model the frequency at which different variations of traits might occur in different sizes of populations.

Strategy

You will model the effect of geographic isolation on the frequency of variations of a trait in a population.

You will infer the risks and benefits of geographic isolation.

Materials

index cards   paper bags
markers—10 different colors

Procedure

1. The class will be divided into groups.
   Geographically isolated populations:
   groups containing 2 students
   Large populations: groups containing 3–8 students

2. Assign a number to each member of the group. Start with one, and continue until every member of the group has a number. Your teacher will distribute 5 index cards to each student.

3. Mark your index cards according to your assigned number:

one—red	five—orange
two—blue	six—yellow
three—green	seven—purple
four—black	eight—brown

4. Shuffle all marked index cards and place them into one paper bag.

5. The color on each card represents a variation of one trait. Without looking, pull 10 index cards from the bag to represent 10 individuals. Record in the data table below the percent of your group's population that has each of the chosen variations. Return all cards to the bag. Repeat five times, recording your results each time.

6. Meet with a member of a different group and share results, so that everyone has information about both types of populations.

Data and Observations

Trials	Red	Blue	Green	Black	Orange	Yellow	Purple	Brown
1								
2								
3								
4								
5								

 SCI 4.g. Students know how to explain significant developments and extinctions of plant and animal life on the geologic time scale. Also covers **SCI 4.f.**

Laboratory Activity 2 (continued)

Questions and Conclusions

1. What can you conclude about the percentage of individuals that might have a particular variation of a trait in large populations? In isolated populations?

_____

_____

_____

2. What would be the effect on the population if the variation represented by red cards was harmful? Which group would have a greater percentage of the population harmed by this variation?

_____

_____

_____

3. What would be the effect on the geographically isolated population if the variation represented by purple cards is harmful? The large population?

_____

_____

_____

4. Using an index card system, tell how you could model the following:
   a. a population of fish in a lake that dries up, forming two separate ponds

   _____

   _____

   b. a population of birds that migrates to an island that contains a population of the same species

   _____

   _____

   c. several birds blown off course while migrating, and settling in a new area

   _____

   _____

Strategy Check

_____ Can you model a geographically isolated population?

_____ Can you describe positive and negative effects of geographic isolation?

LAB 1 Laboratory Activity

Balanced Levers

SCI 6.i. Students know how levers confer mechanical advantage and how the application of this principle applies to the musculoskeletal system.

In general, a lever is a bar that is free to turn about a pivot point called a fulcrum. When a lever is balanced horizontally, the following relationship exists:

$$output\ force \times output\ arm = input\ force \times input\ arm$$
This equation is called the law of the lever.

You can use the principle of balanced levers to construct a mobile. Each of the dowel rods you will use in constructing your mobile acts as a lever. The point where each string supports a dowel rod is the fulcrum of the lever. The weights that you hang from the dowel rods to keep the lever in balance act on the objects as input and output forces. The distances between the objects and the fulcrum correspond to the input arm and output arm of the balanced lever.

Strategy

You will design and construct a mobile.
You will show that each lever in your mobile obeys the law of the lever.

Materials

string
meterstick
4 wooden dowel rods (one 50 cm long, the others at various shorter lengths)
various objects of different weights (paper clips, keys, etc.)
metric spring scale (calibrated in newtons)

Procedure

1. Tie a piece of string near the center of the 50 cm dowel. Anchor the other end of the string to the tabletop or ceiling, if possible. Allow room below this dowel to add objects to the mobile.

2. Weigh each object that you plan to use in constructing your mobile. Record the weights of the objects in Table 1. Be sure to include the smaller dowel rods when you weigh the objects.

3. Use the string and remaining rods to construct the mobile. You may use any design. However, the main lever (50-cm rod) and any other dowels you use must be balanced horizontally. See Figure 1.

4. When you are finished, measure the distance in mm from each hanging object to the fulcrum of each lever. When recording these distances in Table 2, choose one distance on the balanced lever as the output arm and the other as the input arm. Thus, the weight of the object hanging from the output arm is the output force. The weight of the object hanging from the input arm is the input force.

Figure 1

Laboratory Activity 1 (continued)

Data and Observations

For each lever, calculate the product of the output force and the output arm and the product of the input force and the input arm. Record your calculations in Table 2. Use your calculations to support the law of the lever.

Table 1

Object	Weight (N)	Object	Weight (N)

Table 2

Lever	Input arm (mm)	Input force (N)	Product (N × mm)	Output arm (mm)	Output force (N)	Product (N × mm)
A						
B						
C						
D						

Questions and Conclusions

1. A 25-N weight hangs 10 cm to the left of the fulcrum of a lever. A 15-N weight hangs 12 cm to the right of the fulcrum. Is the lever balanced? How do you know?

_____

_____

_____

2. How does the length of string used to hang the objects affect their position on the lever?

_____

_____

_____

Laboratory Activity 1 (continued)

3. When is an equal arm balance an example of a balanced lever?

_____

_____

_____

4. For the balanced levers shown in Figure 2, use the law of the levers to fill in the missing data for **a** and **b.**

Figure 2

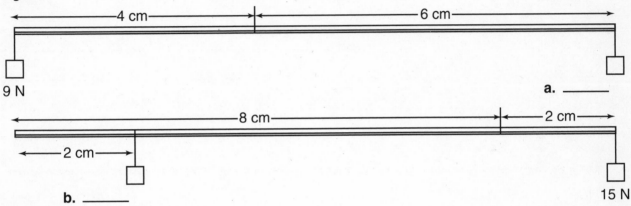

Strategy Check

_____ Can you design and construct a working mobile?

_____ Can you show that each lever in your mobile obeys the law of the lever?

Analyzing Bones

LAB 2 Laboratory Activity

The skeletal system provides support for the body and protection for internal organs. In order to provide these functions, bones must be hard and strong. Scientists have discovered that the element calcium is responsible for making bones strong. Adding calcium to a bone can make it stronger, while removing calcium will make the bone weak and brittle. The amount of calcium in bones can change over time. Certain types of hard physical exercise and work can result in a gain of calcium to bones, while certain diseases and diets can result in a loss of calcium from bones.

Strategy

You will test the hardness of chicken bones before and after soaking them in different liquids. You will hypothesize which solutions will remove calcium from bones and test your hypothesis.

Materials

hydrogen peroxide
water
vinegar
a liquid chosen by the student
4 beakers or jars
chicken leg bones (boiled and cleaned)
forceps

WARNING: *Wear gloves throughout this experiment. Do not taste, eat, or drink any materials used in the lab. Inform your teacher if you come into contact with any chemicals.*

Procedure

1. Four liquids will be tested for their effects on bones. Three of these liquids are listed in Table 1. You should choose a fourth liquid to test (lemon juice, fruit juices, soft drinks, milk, and so forth). Have your choice approved by your teacher and then record the type of liquid in Table 1 in Data and Observations.

2. Make a hypothesis about the effects each liquid will have on the strength of chicken bones. Write your hypothesis in Table 1.

3. Check the hardness of a chicken bone by gently twisting and bending the bone. Be careful not to crack or break the bone. Write your observations on the lines provided in the Data and Observations section.

4. Fill each beaker with one of the liquids. Label the beakers with your name and the kind of liquid.

5. Place a bone in each beaker of liquid. After 10 min, observe the bones and record in Table 2 any changes that you see.

6. After 48–72 h, use forceps to remove the bones from the liquids. Rinse the bones with water and observe them carefully. Record your observations in Table 2.

7. Retest the bones for hardness by twisting and bending. Record the results of the test in the Results column of Table 1.

SCI 5.c. Students know how bones and muscles work together to provide a structural framework for movement.

Laboratory Activity 2 (continued)

Data and Observations
Table 1

Liquid	Hypothesis	Results
Water		
Vinegar		
Hydrogen peroxide		

Original Observations of bone hardness:
Table 2

Liquid	Observations (after 10 min)	Observations (after 48–72 h)
Water		
Vinegar		
Hydrogen peroxide		

Questions and Conclusions
1. What liquids removed calcium from bone?

_____

_____

_____

_____

Laboratory Activity 2 (continued)

2. How accurate were your hypotheses for the effects of each liquid?

_____

_____

_____

3. A baby's bones are softer than a teenager's. What might be a reason for this?

_____

_____

_____

4. Some older persons suffer from a disease called osteoporosis, which results from calcium loss in bones. The bones weaken and are more likely to break. One way to help prevent osteoporosis is to eat calcium-rich foods. What foods could you eat to obtain more calcium?

_____

_____

_____

_____

5. Scientists have discovered that astronauts lose bone calcium while they are exposed to the microgravity of space. What might be a reason for this and what could astronauts do to prevent or slow the loss of calcium?

_____

_____

_____

_____

Strategy Check

_____ Can you test the hardness of chicken bones before and after soaking them in different liquids?

_____ Can you hypothesize which solutions will remove calcium from bones and test your hypothesis?

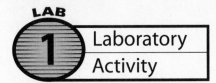

Blood Pressure

The main blood vessels of the body are the arteries and the veins. The heart pumps blood to all parts of the body by way of arteries. Veins carry blood back to the heart. Blood within your blood vessels is under pressure. Do arteries and veins have the same blood pressure?

Strategy

You will build an artificial heart and blood vessels with a plastic squeeze bottle and glass and rubber tubing.

You will measure and record the distance that water squirts from the glass tube and rubber tube.

You will compare the distance water squirts from each tube to the softness of the tubes.

Materials

food coloring (red)

2 glass tubes, 20 cm long and 5 cm long, 5-mm inside diameter, inserted in a rubber stopper (2-hole) by your teacher

meterstick

rubber tube, 18 cm long, 5-mm inside diameter

squeeze bottle

wash pan

Procedure

1. Fill a squeeze bottle with water. Add several drops of red food coloring to the water and shake gently.

2. Put the rubber stopper, with tubes attached, into the squeeze bottle opening. The stopper should fit tightly.

3. Rest a meterstick lengthwise on the edges of a washpan. Hold the rubber tube on one edge of the washpan. The rubber tube should be level with the glass tube. See Figure 2.

Figure 1

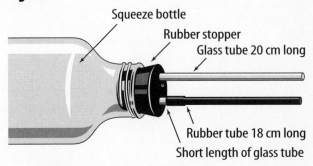

Squeeze bottle
Rubber stopper
Glass tube 20 cm long
Rubber tube 18 cm long
Short length of glass tube

4. While a classmate squeezes the bottle, determine how far the water stream from each tube travels. Record your result in Table 1.

5. Refill the bottle before each new trial and repeat steps 3 and 4 three more times. Again record the results in the table.

Figure 2

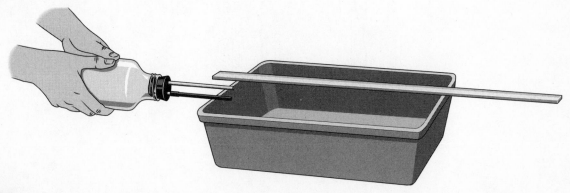

SCI 6.j. Students know that contractions of the heart generate blood pressure and that heart valves prevent backflow of blood in the circulatory system.

Copyright © Glencoe/McGraw-Hill, a division of The McGraw-Hill Companies, Inc.

Laboratory Activity 1 (continued)

Data and Observations

1. Record your results in Table 1. Use centimeter units.

Table 1

Trial	1	2	3	4	Average
1. Glass tube					
2. Rubber tube					

2. Calculate the average distance water travels for each tube. Record the average in the table.

Questions and Conclusions

1. The higher the pressure in a tube, the farther water will travel when it comes out of the tube. In which tube was water pressure higher? In which tube was water pressure lower?

_____

_____

2. Veins are soft and flexible, while arteries are tougher and less flexible. Which tube corresponds to arteries? Which tube corresponds to veins?

_____

_____

3. Using your results, compare blood pressure in arteries to blood pressure in veins.

_____

_____

4. What part of your body can be compared to the squeeze bottle? The water?

_____

_____

Laboratory Activity 1 (continued)

Blood pressure is described by measuring two events: (**a**) Systolic pressure—pressure when the ventricles of the heart contract and push blood into arteries (**b**) Diastolic pressure—pressure when the ventricles relax and blood in the arteries is not being pushed.

Blood pressure is a comparison of systolic to diastolic numbers. Figure 3 shows blood pressure measured in mm of mercury compared with age in years. For example, the systolic pressure for a 10-year-old child is 100 mm of mercury. The diastolic pressure for this child is 65 mm of mercury.

Figure 3

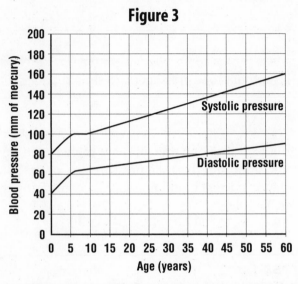

5. a. What is the systolic pressure for a 20-year-old person? _____

b. What is the diastolic pressure for a 20-year-old person? _____

6. From the graph, determine the blood pressure for the following ages: (list systolic, then diastolic.)

a. 15 years old _____

_____

b. 30 years old _____

_____

c. 40 years old _____

_____

7. a. How much change occurs in systolic pressure from age 0 to 60?

_____

b. How much change occurs in diastolic pressure from age 0 to 60?

_____

Laboratory Activity 1 (continued)

8. Does systolic blood pressure change more from age 0 to 20 than from age 20 to 60?

_____

9. a. At what age is there the greatest difference between systolic pressure and diastolic pressure?

_____

b. What is the blood pressure at this age? _____

_____

10. The age of a person with a systolic pressure of 120 and diastolic pressure of 75 should be close to what?

_____

A person is said to have high blood pressure if systolic and diastolic pressures are higher than normal. A person is said to have a low blood pressure if systolic and diastolic pressure are lower than normal. Record if the following people have *high, low,* or *normal* blood pressure by comparing the pressure in Table 2 with those in the graph in Figure 3.

Table 2

Blood Pressure			
Age	**Systolic**	**Diastolic**	**Pressure**
45	140	83	**11.**
30	130	85	**12.**
60	140	80	**13.**

Strategy Check

_____ Did you build an artificial heart and blood vessels?

_____ Did you determine which tube, glass or rubber, allows the water to squirt out farther when the bottle is squeezed?

_____ Can you correlate the distance water squirts to the softness of the rubber and glass tubes?

LAB 2 Laboratory Activity

Heart Structure

SCI 6.j. Students know that contractions of the heart generate blood pressure and that heart valves prevent backflow of blood in the circulatory system. Also covers **SCI 5.b.**

Can you name the part of your body that is a muscle, works on its own without any reminder from you, pushes about five liters of liquid through your body each minute, relaxes for only about half a second, and squeezes or contracts 70 to 100 times a minute? The organ described is the human heart.

Strategy

You will observe the outside and inside of a cow or sheep heart to locate and label the parts of a heart.

You will study the direction of blood flow through the heart.

You will review the condition of blood on the right side of the heart as compared with the blood on the left side. Discuss side reversal in detail with the class to avoid confusion.

Materials

2 colored pencils (red and blue)
dissecting pan
dissecting probe
heart (sheep or cow)
narrow tongue depressors
coffee stirrers
Alternate materials

Procedure

Part A—Outside of Heart

1. Position your sheep or cow heart in a dissecting pan so that it matches Figure 1. **WARNING:** *Wash hands thoroughly after handling heart.*
   NOTE: Use the description below and the directions of arrows in Figure 2 to help locate each part of the heart. Use Figure 2 to label each part as you identify it.

2. The *superior and inferior vena cava* returns blood to the right side of the heart from body organs. Locate and label the *superior and inferior vena cava.* The pulmonary vein returns blood to the left side of the heart from the lungs. Locate and label the *pulmonary vein.*

3. Blood in veins enters the right and left atrium, two small chambers at the top of the heart. Locate and label the *right atrium and left atrium.*

4. Pumping action of the heart squeezes blood from the atria into the right and left ventricles, two large chambers at the bottom of the heart. Locate and label the *right ventricle and left ventricle.*

Figure 1

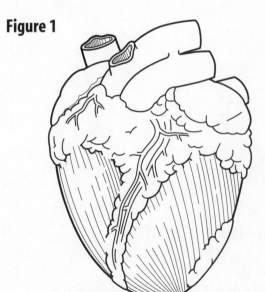

5. Pumping action of the heart squeezes blood from the two ventricles. Blood leaves the heart on the left side by way of an artery called the *aorta.* Locate and label the aorta, which carries blood to all body parts. Blood leaves the heart on the right side by way of another artery, the pulmonary artery. Locate and label the *pulmonary artery,* which carries blood to the lungs.

Laboratory Activity 2 (continued)

Figure 2

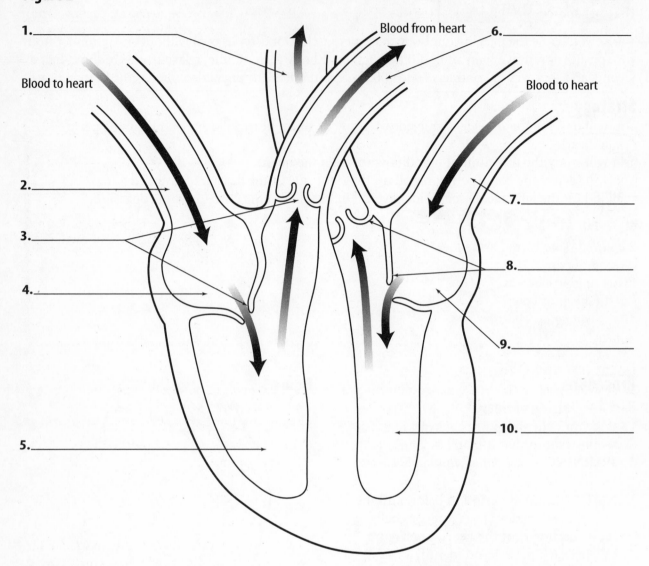

1._____

Blood to heart

Blood from heart

6._____

Blood to heart

2._____

3._____

4._____

7._____

8._____

9._____

5._____

10._____

Part B—Inside of Heart

1. Your teacher will slice open the heart with a scalpel.
2. Note the thickness of the muscle that makes up the left and right ventricles.
3. Locate and label the *heart valves* between atria and ventricles. Valves keep blood flowing in one direction.
4. Locate and label the valves where the pulmonary artery and aorta are joined to the heart.

Part C—Condition of Blood in Heart

1. Use a blue pencil to color in the spaces on Figure 2 to show where *deoxygenated blood* would be. Blood returning to or pumped from the right side of the heart is deoxygenated. This means that the amount of oxygen in the blood is low.
2. Use a red pencil to color in spaces to show where oxygenated blood would be. Oxygenated blood contains a large amount of oxygen. Those vessels returning to or leaving the left side of the heart carry *oxygenated blood.*

Laboratory Activity 2 (continued)

Data and Observations

1. Label and color Figure 2 as instructed in the Procedure. **NOTE:** Notice that Figure 2 shows the left and right sides of the heart reversed. The diagram actually shows the position of the heart in a person as it would appear if you were facing that person whose heart is shown.
2. Complete Table 1. Use the words *oxygenated* or *deoxygenated* to describe the condition of the blood in each part. (See Part C of the Procedure.)

Table 1

Part	Right side	Left side
Atrium		
Ventricle		
Vena cava		
Aorta		
Pulmonary vein		
Pulmonary artery		

Questions and Conclusions

1. To what part of the body is blood pumped as it passes through the pulmonary artery?

_____

2. From what part of the body is blood being returned to the heart as it passes through the pulmonary veins? Through the vena cava?

_____

_____

3. If blood leaves the right side of the heart deoxygenated and returns to the left side oxygenated, what gas has been added to the blood? Through what organ must the blood pass in order to change in this way?

_____

_____

4. Explain why the muscle of the left ventricle is thicker than the muscle of the right ventricle.

_____

_____

5. Explain the function of the heart valves.

_____

_____

Laboratory Activity 2 (continued)

6. List in order those parts that determine the direction of blood flow through the heart. Start with the vena cava and include the following: left atrium, right atrium, left ventricle, right ventricle, pulmonary artery, pulmonary vein, aorta.

_____

_____

_____

7. Use the data in the Data and Observations section to explain the condition of all blood in
   a. the heart's right side.

_____

_____

   b. the heart's left side.

_____

_____

Strategy Check

_____ Can you locate and properly label the following parts of the heart: vena cava, right atrium, left atrium, pulmonary artery, pulmonary vein, left ventricle, right ventricle, aorta?

_____ Can you rearrange the above parts in proper order starting with the vena cava to show the direction of blood flow through the heart?

_____ Can you compare the condition of the blood on the right side of the heart to the blood on the left side?

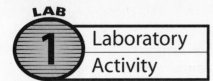

LAB 1 Laboratory Activity

Parts of the Eye

Your eye is one of the most complex organs of your body. Much could be learned about eye functions if you could look inside a human eye and study its parts. This is not very practical, but you can study a cow eye. Cow eyes are very much like human eyes. Cow eyes have another advantage—they are bigger than human eyes.

Strategy

You will dissect a preserved cow eye.
You will identify the most important parts of the eye.
You will describe the functions of these eye parts.

Materials

cow eye (preserved)
dissecting pan
scalpel

SCI 6.d. Students know how simple lenses are used in a magnifying glass, the eye, a camera, a telescope, and a microscope. Also covers SCI 5.g.

Procedure

1. Cut away all of the muscle and fat that surround the rear ball part of the eyeball. Use a scalpel to start cutting the muscle and fat from the front toward the back of the eye. Remove only small portions of tissue at a time. **WARNING:** *Use care when cutting to avoid injury.* Do not remove the optic nerve as you trim the eyeball of fat and muscle. (The optic nerve can be seen as a white, round, pencil-thick bundle of nerves surrounded by a dark-colored layer of muscle tissue at the back of the eye.) Use the dash line shown in Figure 1 as a guide to how much muscle and fat must be removed.

2. You are now ready to cut into the eye. Cut in a circular pattern into the eye at the position marked in Figure 1 with X marks. You must cut through a tough outer layer called the sclera.

3. Cut the eye in half, separating the front from the back. A jellylike material will probably fall out as the eye is cut in half. This is the vitreous humor, a transparent jelly that fills the inside of the eye. The lens is a marble-shaped structure that may also fall out of the eye.

4. Place the front portion of the eye with the outside facing down. Use Figure 2B to help you identify the ciliary muscles, iris, pupil, and cornea. Hold the front portion of the eye up to the light and observe the cornea. The cornea will not be completely transparent, but it is transparent in a living eye.

5. Place the back portion of the eye with the inside facing up. Examine the back portion of the eye Figure 2A. You should have the cut surface facing up. You should notice a thin, wrinkled, whitish tissue on the inside along the back. This is the retina. The retina in a living eye is smooth. NOTE: The retina can be removed for closer examination. Observe that it attaches to the back of the eye. This is the blind spot leading to the optic nerve.

Figure 1

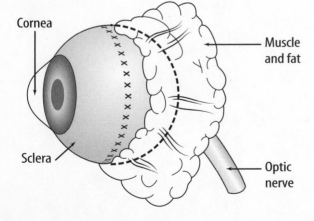

Cornea

Muscle and fat

Sclera

Optic nerve

Laboratory Activity 1 (continued)

6. At the back of the eyeball is a bluish layer called the tapetum. This layer acts as a reflective surface and is found only in certain animals. Push the tapetum aside at its cut edge to find the choroid layer directly below.

7. Examine the solid, round, yellowish structure (Figure 2C) that fell out when you opened the eyeball. This is the lens. It is covered with a layer of fine muscle fibers that control the shape of the lens. Hold it up to the light. The lens does not appear completely transparent now, but it is transparent in a living eye. **WARNING:** *Wash your hands thoroughly after handling the eye.*

8. Correctly label Figure 3 in Data and Observations, which shows the side view diagram of the eye.

9. Record the parts of the eye you identified and their functions in Table 1. You may use reference books and your textbook to complete the table.

Figure 2

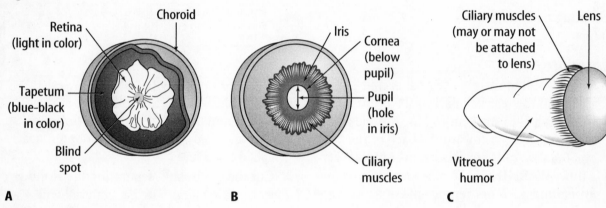

A   B   C

Data and Observations

Figure 3

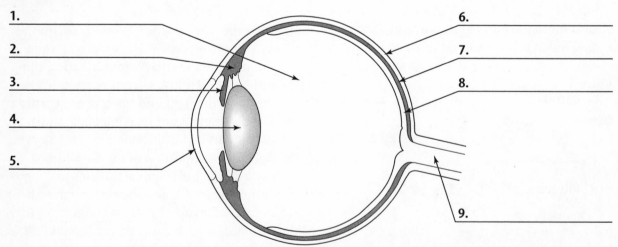

1. _____
2. _____
3. _____
4. _____
5. _____
6. _____
7. _____
8. _____
9. _____

| Laboratory Activity 1 (continued) |

Table 1

<table>
<tr><th colspan="2">Structure of the Eye</th></tr>
<tr><th>Part</th><th>Function</th></tr>
<tr><td>10.</td><td></td></tr>
<tr><td>11.</td><td></td></tr>
<tr><td>12.</td><td></td></tr>
<tr><td>13.</td><td></td></tr>
<tr><td>14.</td><td></td></tr>
<tr><td>15.</td><td></td></tr>
<tr><td>16.</td><td></td></tr>
<tr><td>17.</td><td></td></tr>
<tr><td>18.</td><td></td></tr>
<tr><td>19.</td><td></td></tr>
</table>

Questions and Conclusions

1. Give a possible difference between what you observed in a preserved eye compared with a living eye for the following parts:

   a. retina _____

   _____

   _____

   b. lens _____

   _____

   _____

   c. cornea _____

   _____

   _____

   d. vitreous humor _____

   _____

   _____

Laboratory Activity 1 (continued)

2. List the following eye parts in the order that light passes through them: vitreous humor, retina, lens, cornea, pupil.

_____

_____

3. Explain why it is important that the lens and cornea be transparent in a living eye.

_____

_____

_____

_____

Strategy Check

_____ Did you dissect a preserved cow eye?

_____ Can you identify the most important parts of the eye?

_____ Can you describe the function of each part you examined?

LAB 2 — Laboratory Activity

The Electromagnetic Spectrum

SCI 6.a. Students know visible light is a small band within a very broad electromagnetic spectrum.

There are different types of electromagnetic radiation. The electromagnetic spectrum is used to classify the different types of electromagnetic radiation. Like the periodic table where elements are classified according to their structure, electromagnetic radiation is classified according to wavelengths and frequencies. Although there are different types of electromagnetic radiation, they all travel at the same speed in space, 300,000 km/s. This speed is called the speed of light. Humans are only able to see a small portion of the electromagnetic spectrum, visible light. In this activity, you will create a model of the infrared, visible, and ultraviolet portions of the electromagnetic spectrum. The model you create will be made to scale based on wavelength.

Strategy

You will create a scale model of portions of the electromagnetic spectrum.
You will demonstrate that visible light makes up a very small portion of the electromagnetic spectrum.

Materials

calculator
meterstick or metric ruler (marked in millimeters)
scissors
one piece of paper in each of the following
    colors: red, orange, yellow, green, blue,
    violet, white, and black
black marker
scotch tape
flashlight
prism

Procedure

1. The wavelengths for the visible, infrared, and ultraviolet portions of the spectrum are represented in meters in the table in the Data and Observations section. Complete a metric conversion calculation to find the length of the waves in nanometers. One nanometer is 10^{-9} of a meter so that 10^{-8} m equals 10 nanometers, 10^{-7} m equals 100 nanometers, and 10^{-6} m equals 1,000 nanometers. The scale that will be used to build the model of the spectrum is 1 nanometer equals 1 millimeter. Record your calculations in the table in the Data and Observations section.

2. Work together as a class on the metric conversion calculation for red light. It is good to begin with red light rather than infrared, which is listed first in the data table, because the length of the scale model for infrared light is significantly longer than the scale models of any of the visible light colors.

3. Fill in the scale length in the millimeters column in your data table for red light. This column should always be the same as the final answer for wavelength in nanometers.

4. Use the colored paper to represent the different colors in the visible spectrum. Red paper will be used for the wavelength of red light, orange paper for orange light, and so on. White paper will represent infrared waves, and black paper will represent ultraviolet waves.

5. Cut a strip of red paper that is 2.5 cm wide and the same length as the number you have written in your column for scale length in millimeters.

6. Once you have a strip of red paper that is 750 mm (75 cm) long, mark the actual wavelength of red light, 7.5×10^{-7} m, on the strip.

7. Complete a metric conversion calculation and cut strips for each of the electromagnetic waves represented in the data table. When you have finished, you should have eight strips of paper of different lengths and colors in your model.

8. Align your strips horizontally, directly underneath each other, with the longest strip (which should be infrared) on top and the shortest strip (which should be ultraviolet) on the bottom. Tape all the strips together to make one large sheet.

9. Shine the flashlight through the prism in order to see the visible spectrum.

Laboratory Activity 2 (continued)

Data and Observations

Wave	Actual Wavelength in Meters	Calculation	Actual Wavelength in Nanometers	Scale Wavelength in Millimeters
1. Infrared	1×10^{-6}			
2. Red	7.5×10^{-7}			
3. Orange	6.25×10^{-7}			
4. Yellow	5.75×10^{-7}			
5. Green	5.25×10^{-7}			
6. Blue	4.5×10^{-7}			
7. Violet	4×10^{-7}			
8. Ultraviolet	3×10^{-8}			

Questions and Conclusions

1. What colors did you observe from the prism? List them in order from top to bottom.

_____

_____

_____

2. Why do we use the scale of 1 nanometer equals 1 millimeter?

_____

_____

_____

3. How does the prism verify part of your model?

_____

_____

_____

_____

Laboratory Activity 2 (continued)

4. A television wave is approximately 3 meters long. If we were to make this wave part of our model, how long would the strip of paper representing the television wave have to be?

_____

_____

_____

5. Why didn't you include the whole electromagnetic spectrum in your model?

_____

_____

_____

Strategy Check

_____ Can you compare the wavelength sizes of the electromagnetic spectrum?

_____ Can you demonstrate that visible light is a small portion of the electromagnetic spectrum?

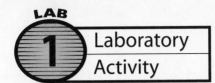

Sound Waves and Pitch

SCI 5.g. Students know how to relate the structures of the eye and ear to their functions.

Sounds are produced and transmitted by vibrating matter. You hear the buzz of a fly because its wings vibrate, the air vibrates, and your eardrum vibrates. The sound of a drum is produced when the drumhead vibrates up and down, the air vibrates, and your eardrum vibrates. Sound is a compressional wave. In a compressional wave, matter vibrates in the same direction as the wave travels. For you to hear a sound, a sound source must produce a compressional wave in matter, such as air. The air transmits the compressional wave to your eardrum, which vibrates in response to the compressional wave.

Compressional waves can be described by amplitude, wavelength, and frequency—the same as transverse waves. The pitch of a sound is related to the frequency of a compressional wave. You are familiar with high pitches and low pitches in music, but people are also able to hear a range of pitches beyond that of musical sounds. People can hear sounds with frequencies between 20 and 20,000 Hz.

Strategy

You will demonstrate that sound is produced by vibrations of matter.
You will vary the pitch of vibrating objects.

Materials

4 rubber bands of different widths but equal lengths
cardboard box, such as a shoe box or cigar box

Safety Precautions

Safety goggles should be worn throughout the experiment.

Procedure

1. Stretch the four rubber bands around a box as shown in Figure 1.

Figure 1

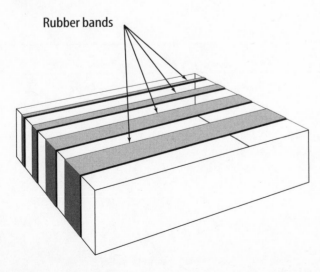

Rubber bands

2. Pluck the first rubber band, allowing it to vibrate. Listen to the pitch of the vibrating rubber band. Predict how the pitches of the other rubber bands will compare with this pitch. Record your prediction in the Data and Observations section. Pluck the remaining rubber bands. Record your observations about the variation in pitch.

3. Remove three rubber bands from the box. Hold the remaining rubber band tightly in the middle with one hand. Pluck it with the other. Move your hand up and down the rubber band to increase or decrease the length of the rubber band that can vibrate. Predict how the pitch will change as you change the length of the vibrating rubber band. Pluck the rubber band for each new length and record your observations of the length of the vibrating rubber band and pitch.

Laboratory Activity 1 (continued)

Data and Observations

1. Prediction of variation in pitch of sounds produced by rubber bands of different widths:

_____

_____

_____

2. Observation of changes in pitch with varying thickness of rubber bands:

_____

_____

_____

3. Observation of changes in pitch with varying length of the rubber band:

_____

_____

_____

Questions and Conclusions

1. How does length affect the pitch of sound produced by a vibrating object?

_____

_____

2. How does the width of a rubber band affect its frequency of vibration?

_____

_____

3. Based on your results, how would you expect the pitch of sound produced by a vibrating string to be affected by the length of the string?

_____

_____

Strategy Check

_____ Can you demonstrate that sound is produced by vibrations of matter?

_____ Can you vary the pitch of vibrating objects?

Musical Instruments

LAB 2 — Laboratory Activity

Musical instruments have been made and used for thousands of years by different cultures around the world. String, brass, woodwind, and percussion instruments all produce their own distinctive musical sounds. In this activity, you can make and compare the sounds made by several simple instruments.

Strategy

You will construct simple musical instruments.
You will compare and contrast the sounds made by these instruments.
You will classify the instruments according to their type.

Materials

block of wood, 15 cm × 10 cm × 5 cm
wire coat hanger
wire cutters
wire staples
hammer
6 beakers of the same size
wooden spoon
water
shoe box or tissue box
2 pieces of wood, 1 cm × 1 cm × 15 cm
5 rubber bands of varying lengths and thicknesses
6 nails of varying lengths, 5 cm to 20 cm

meterstick
string, 90 cm
scissors
metal spoon
2 plastic soda bottles with lids
dried peas, small pebbles, uncooked rice, or paper clips
plastic trash bag
string
tape
empty containers such as margarine tubs, plastic bowls, or cardboard tubes

Procedure

Part A—Twanger

1. Use wire cutters to cut a coat hanger into four or five pieces of different lengths. The lengths of the pieces should vary from 8 cm to 20 cm.
2. Use wire staples and a hammer to attach the lengths of wire to the wooden block, as shown in Figure 1.

Figure 1

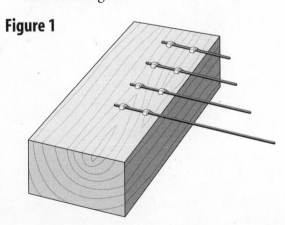

3. Pluck the wires with your thumb or a pen. In the data table in the Data and Observations section, describe the sounds and pitches produced by the various pieces of wire.

Part B—Xylophone

4. Set up six beakers of the same size in a row.
5. Leave the first beaker empty. Add increasing amounts of water to each of the remaining five beakers. The third beaker should be about half full and the last beaker should be almost full.
6. Tap the side of each beaker gently with a wooden spoon. Describe the sounds and pitches produced by each of the beakers.

 SCI 7.c. Communicate the logical connection among hypotheses, science concepts, tests conducted, data collected, and conclusions drawn from the scientific evidence.

Laboratory Activity 2 (continued)

Part C—Guitar

7. Stretch the rubber bands around the box lengthwise.

8. With a partner's help, slide one piece of wood under the rubber bands at one end of the box. Slide the other piece of wood under the rubber bands at the other end of the box. Your completed guitar should look like Figure 2.

9. Pluck the rubber bands with your fingers. Describe the sounds and pitches produced by each of the rubber bands.

Part D—Nail Chimes

10. Cut a piece of string into 15-cm pieces. Tie each piece of string around the meterstick, leaving a long end hanging down.

11. Tie the hanging end of each string around the head of a nail. Arrange the nails from shortest to longest.

12. Suspend the meterstick between two chairs or tables, as shown in Figure 3. Be sure the nails don't touch each other.

13. Use a metal spoon to tap the nails. Describe the sounds and pitches produced by each of the nails.

Figure 2

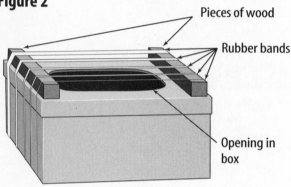

Pieces of wood

Rubber bands

Opening in box

Figure 3

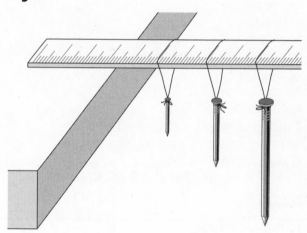

Laboratory Activity 2 (continued)

Part E—Shakers

14. Place a small amount of dried peas, small pebbles, uncooked rice, or paper clips into one plastic bottle. Screw the cap on the bottle.

15. Place a small amount of another material in a second plastic bottle and screw on the cap.

16. Shake each bottle or tap it against your hand. Describe the sounds made by each shaker.

Part F—Drums

17. Cut down the sides of the plastic bag to make one large sheet.

18. Place one of your containers open side down on the plastic sheet. Cut around the container, leaving about an extra 10 cm all around the container.

19. With a partner, stretch the plastic tightly over the top of the container. Use string and tape to hold the plastic in place, as shown in Figure 4.

20. Repeat steps 18 and 19 with a container of a different size.

21. Hit the top of your drums lightly with your fingers or a pencil. Describe the sounds made by each drum.

Figure 4

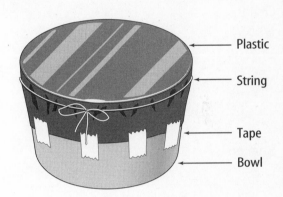

Plastic
String
Tape
Bowl

Laboratory Activity 2 (continued)

Data and Observations

Instrument	Sounds and pitches
Twanger	
Xylophone	
Guitar	
Nail chimes	
Shakers	
Drums	

Questions and Conclusions

1. Which instruments were able to produce sounds of different pitches?

_____

2. What caused the different pitches of sounds in each of those instruments?

_____

3. Classify each of the instruments you made by type.

_____

_____

4. How does the length of a piece of wire or a nail affect its frequency of vibration?

_____

Strategy Check

_____ Can you construct simple musical instruments?

_____ Can you compare and contrast the sounds made by these instruments?

_____ Can you classify the instruments according to their type?

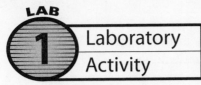

LAB 1 Laboratory Activity

Fetal Development

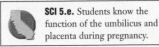

SCI 5.e. Students know the function of the umbilicus and placenta during pregnancy.

A human body usually develops inside its mother for 38 weeks. During the first eight weeks it is called an embryo. From the ninth to the thirty-eighth week it is called a fetus. Different organs and systems develop at different times during these 38 weeks. The age of a developing baby can be determined by its length.

Strategy

You will measure the length of five diagrams of a human fetus.
You will match events taking place during development with the proper age of the fetus.

Materials

ruler (metric)

Procedure

1. Measure the length of each fetus from crown to rump. Record in Table 3.
2. To determine actual length, multiply each measurement by 2.75. Record in Table 3.
3. Record the events occurring to each fetus in Table 2. Events are listed in Table 1.

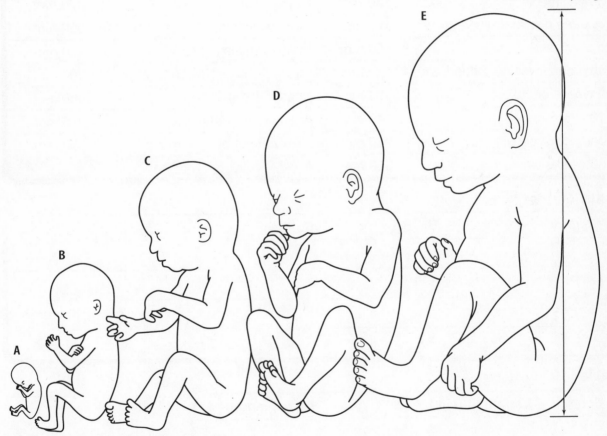

Crown to rump length

Questions and Conclusions

1. Explain the changes that take place in a fetus between week 9 and week 38.

   a. body hair _____

   b. the eyes _____

   c. sex determination _____

Laboratory Activity 1 (continued)

2. A fetus born with a crown to rump length of 270 mm will have a difficult time of survival.

   About how old is a fetus of this length? _____

3. It is possible to "see" a fetus using ultrasound equipment. How might ultrasounds taken at

   9 and 20 weeks of age differ? _____

Strategy Check

_____ Can you measure the crown to rump length of a fetus diagram?

_____ Can you match events during development with specific ages of a fetus?

Data and Observations

Table 1

Event	Length	Event	Length
24 weeks old	230 mm	eyes open	300 mm
sex can be determined	140 mm	32 weeks old	300 mm
eyes closed	50 mm	mother feels movement	140 mm
all organs well developed	230 mm	body "chubby" looking	300 mm
9 weeks old	50 mm	body hair is gone	360 mm
16 weeks old	140 mm	can grasp with hand	360 mm
body covered with hair	230 mm	sex cannot be determined	50 mm
38 weeks old	360 mm		

Table 2

A	B	C	D	E

Table 3

Fetus	Length in (mm)	× 2.75	Actual length
A		× 2.75	
B		× 2.75	
C		× 2.75	
D		× 2.75	
E		× 2.75	

Modeling Cell Division in Early Development

Every person starts out as a single cell. Cell division is responsible for the development of a baby from the single cell. As the single cell begins developing, cell division results in exponential growth in the number of cells present. Exponential growth is growth that occurs at an ever-increasing rate. On a graph, exponential growth is represented by a J-shaped curve.

Strategy

You will model how cell division results in exponential growth in the number of cells in a developing human.

You will determine why exponential growth cannot continue indefinitely during human development.

You will infer why uncontrolled cell division, which occurs in cancer, can be so harmful to human health.

Materials

uncooked rice
paper cups (11)
graph paper

Procedure

1. Obtain a container of uncooked rice from your teacher. Each grain of rice represents one human cell.
2. Place one grain of rice in a paper cup. This grain of rice represents the single cell that results when sperm and egg unite.
3. Label paper cups 1 through 10, and place them in a row next to the cup containing the original cell. During the first 10 cell divisions, the cells in the developing human all have the same cell-cycle length.
4. Place two grains of rice into cup 1 to represent the number of cells present after the original cell undergoes the first round of mitosis. Record the number *2* in the table in the Data and Observations section.

5. Place grains of rice into cup 2 to represent the number of cells that will be present after the second round of mitosis. Record the number of cells in your data table.
6. Repeat step 5 for cups 3 through 10.
7. Using your data and graph paper, make a line graph that shows the growth in the numbers of cells. Label the x-axis *Number of cell divisions* and the y-axis *Number of cells*.

SCI 5.d. Students know how the reproductive organs of the human female and male generate eggs and sperm and how sexual activity may lead to fertilization and pregnancy.

Laboratory Activity 2 (continued)

Data and Observations

Growth in Cell Number Due to Mitosis			
Number of mitotic divisions	Resulting number of cells	Number of mitotic divisions	Resulting number of cells
1		6	
2		7	
3		8	
4		9	
5		10	

Questions and Conclusions

1. Initially all of the cells in a developing human have the same cell-cycle length. After the eleventh round of mitosis, groups of cells begin to have different cell-cycle lengths. What step of the cell cycle is likely to be longer in cells with a longer cell cycle?

_____

_____

2. Could the type of growth you modeled with grains of rice continue indefinitely in a developing human? Explain your answer.

_____

_____

3. Cancer results from uncontrolled cell division. Using your results from this activity, infer why cancer can have such a serious effect on human health.

_____

_____

Strategy Check

_____ Can you describe exponential growth?

_____ Can you graphically represent exponential growth?

_____ Can you describe how cell division results in exponential growth?

Inquiry Activities

1 Inquiry Activity

It's a Small World

SCI 1.b. Students know the characteristics that distinguish plant cells from animal cells, including chloroplasts and cell walls.

What do you think of when someone mentions ocean life? Most people think of fish, sharks, whales, and seaweed. But what would you say if you were told none of these living things could survive without microscopic organisms? How could something so small be so important? Microorganisms (microscopic living things) are important in oxygen production during photosynthesis and are the first link in many food chains.

Materials

- microscope
- slides and coverslips
- prepared slides of diatoms

- live specimens of mixed algae, mixed protozoa, and/or pond water and tide pool H_2O samples

What You'll Investigate

In this activity, you will observe microorganisms under a microscope.

Procedure

WARNING: *Be careful of glass slides breaking and cutting you. Be careful plugging in the microscope.*

1. Recall the differences between plant cells and animal cells.
2. Write a hypothesis that states if you will find both animal & plant cells in the pond H_2O, tide pool H_2O, or both. Include why this will happen.
3. Design an experiment using slides of cells from pond H_2O, tide pools, and pre-made slides.

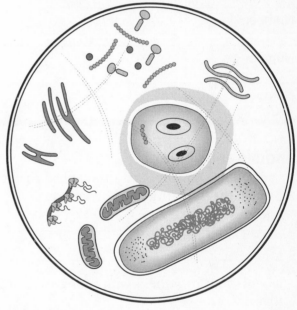

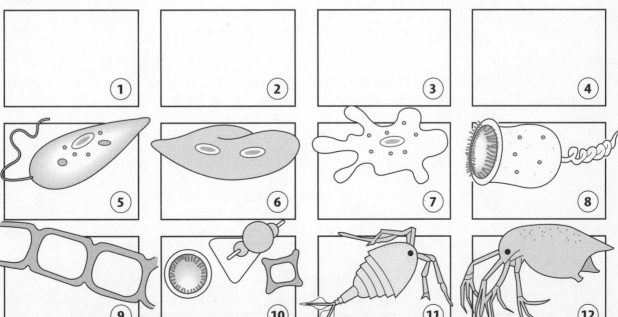

| Inquiry Activity 1 (continued) |

4. Follow your teacher's guidelines for using a microscope.

5. View slides from pond and tide pool samples.

6. Draw slides of organisms you observed.

7. Use the *Data and Observations* table to record characteristics of each microorganism.

Data and Observations

Microorganism	Tide Pool Water	Pond Water
Number		
Number		
Number		
Number		
Number		

Conclude and Apply

1. Did you find microorganisms that had characteristics of plant cells, animals cells, or both? Explain the similarities and differences.

_____

_____

2. Discuss your hypothesis with your group. Decide if your observations supported your hypothesis. Explain.

_____

_____

3. What change could you make in your experimental design to determine if cells are neither plants nor animals?

_____

_____

Going Further

Research what kinds of animals depend and feed on plankton in the ocean and any special methods they have for catching their prey.

LAB 2 Inquiry Activity

Getting to the Root of It

SCI 5.a. Students know plants and animals have levels of organization for structure and function, including cells, tissues, organs, organ systems, and the whole organism.

Earth's land is constantly changing as surface materials wear away and move from one place to another. This process is called erosion and is usually brought about by the action of wind, water, glaciers, and gravity. In this activity you will find out how the roots of plants affect the rate of soil erosion.

Materials

- pencil
- pots (with drainage holes)
- potting soil
- corn seeds
- water spray bottle
- plant light, window, or other light source

What You'll Investigate

In this activity, you will design and complete an experiment to test the effects of roots on soil erosion.

Procedure

WARNING: *Seeds are sometimes treated with a fungicide chemical. You should not put the seeds in your mouth, and you should wash your hands after handling them.*

1. Consider a field of corn that is planted in rows. Write three questions that relate to the plants and erosion that can be investigated with an experiment.

2. Write a hypothesis that states how some part(s) of the corn plant might affect rainfall on the field and the resulting flow of water.

3. Design an experiment to see if your hypothesis can be supported. Use any or all of the materials listed to complete your investigation.

4. Soak five to ten corn seeds in water for 24 hours.

5. Plant the corn seeds as directed in your procedure. Place pots under plant light or near window.

6. After plants have grown, use a sprinkling can or spray bottle to make rain.

7. Repeat this procedure the next day.

8. Record your data and that of the other teams in the *Data and Observations* table on the next page.

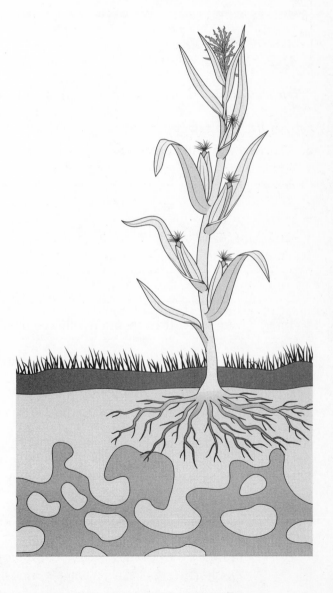

Inquiry Activity 2 (continued)

Data and Observations

Team	Soil loss with plant	Soil loss without plant	Key
1.			
2.			
3.			++ extensive
4.			+ moderate
5.			0 minimal
6.			

Conclude and Apply

1. Did you have erosion in any of your pots? Explain.

_____

_____

2. What do you think roots do for the soil?

_____

_____

3. Compare corn plant roots to tree roots.

_____

_____

4. Infer: Severe forest fires are often followed by mud slides. Why?

_____

_____

5. Based on what you have learned in this lab, what might be a consequence of deforestation?

_____

_____

Going Further

Research how the destruction of rain forests affects the soil. What are some of the short-term effects? What are some long-term effects?

LAB 3 Inquiry Activity

Survival in Extreme Climates

To survive in a desert environment, plants and animals must have special adaptations. The shifts of air temperature within 24 hours—daytime highs of up to 35°C to 50°C in the summer and nighttime lows of 5°C to 25°C—are the most extreme of any of the climate types found on Earth. Deserts are also the driest environments on Earth, often getting less than 25 cm of rainfall in a year. Despite the high temperatures and lack of rainfall, many plants and animals live in the desert.

Materials

- plastic covering or newspaper
- plastic pots
- three–five different types of house plants, such as ferns, different flowering plants, one or two types of small cactus plants per group
- sand
- clay
- cactus soil

What You'll Investigate

In this activity, you will observe how cactus plants differ from other types of plants and how adaptations of cactus plants allow them to survive in desert conditions.

Procedure

1. List several characteristics desert plants have that help them survive in extreme temperatures.
2. Compare three plants from the selection. Decide which of the plants can survive in desert conditions.
3. Design a simulation of a desert ecosystem.
4. Determine soil for plants: sand, clay, sand and clay, cactus soil.
5. Put a small amount of water in the soil. Plant three plants.
6. Do not water again. Observe for 7–10 days.

SCI 4.f. Students know how movements of Earth's continental and oceanic plates through time, with associated changes in climate and geographic connections, have affected the past and present distribution of organisms.

Inquiry Activity 3 (continued)

Data and Observations

Day	Plant choice	Soil choice

Conclude and Apply

1. What structures are unique to the cactus plants?

   _____

   _____

2. How do you think these structures helped the cactus to grow and live?

   _____

   _____

3. What factors in a desert environment support cacti but not ferns and flowering house plants?

   _____

   _____

Going Further

Research a different type of environment, such as a forest near a lake or an inland mountain range, and gather information about some of the main types of plants found there. Consider what adaptations these plants may have made in order to survive in the climate in that environment. Collect and examine some plants on site to see whether your hypotheses are correct. Replant the plants when you are through.

LAB 4 Inquiry Activity

Radiation and Its Effects on Seeds

SCI 3.e. Students know that extinction of a species occurs when the environment changes and the adaptive characteristics of a species are insufficient for its survival.

One source of electrical power for human use is nuclear power. Nuclear power plants can be found around the world. Usually, these are safe areas, but sometimes there is a leak into the surrounding soil, air, or water. What do you think happens to the crops in the fields nearby? When seeds are exposed to nuclear radiation, many changes can be observed. Seeds contain genetic material that determines the characteristics of the plants they produce. Radiation can change this genetic material. The type of seed and the amount of radiation absorbed determine the extent of this change.

Materials

- boxes or containers for planting
- potting soil
- a few seeds that have not been irradiated
- seeds that have received different amounts of radiation (irradiated seeds)

What You'll Investigate

In this activity, you will grow plants from seeds that have been exposed to different amounts of nuclear radiation. The growth patterns of these plants will be observed and recorded during a period of weeks. The results of your experiment will be used to discuss some possible effects of exposure to nuclear radiation.

Procedure

1. Discuss with your groups what you think might be some effects on seeds that have been irradiated. List some of your ideas. Read step 5 to help you with ideas.
2. Write a hypothesis that states what differences you will find in the plants that do or do not grow from the seeds. Remember that the seeds have been exposed to different amounts of radiation.
3. It is important that all seeds are planted and grown under the same conditions. Plant the seeds according to your teacher's instructions. Plant one container of untreated seeds. Label this *Container 1*. Carefully label each of the remaining containers. On a separate sheet of paper, create a table similar to **Table 1**. Record the number of each container and the radiation exposures of each container's seeds.
4. Place the containers in a location away from drafts where they can receive as much light as possible. Keep the soil moist, but not wet, at all times.

5. Record your observations in a table similar to **Table 2**. As soon as the first seeds sprout, start recording your observations. Observe the plants at regular intervals for several weeks. Watch for differences in sprouting and growth rates and differences in size, color, shape, number, and location of stems and leaves. Remember, it is important to make an entry in the table for each container at every observation date, even if you report no change.
6. Include in your observations sketches of your plants. Show any differences in growth patterns.

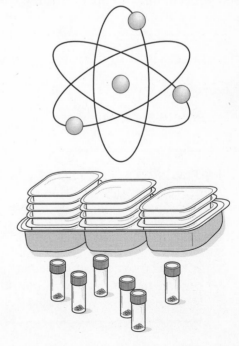

Inquiry Activity 4 (continued)

Data and Observations
Table 1

Container number	Amount of radiation
1	no radiation

Table 2

Date	Container number	Observations
	1	

Conclude and Apply

1. Why did you plant seeds that were not exposed to nuclear radiation?

_____

2. What patterns did you observe as the seeds sprouted? In the growth rate of the plants?

_____

3. What characteristics of the plants seemed to be the most affected? Least affected?

_____

4. What conclusions can you make based on the results of this experiment?

_____

5. Low-level radiation is sometimes used in food processing. What might be the purpose of this?

_____

Going Further
Design an experiment to determine if there is a difference in the effect of exposing seeds to a large amount of radiation in a short period of time or smaller amounts over a longer period of time.

LAB 5 — Inquiry Activity

Pass the Sugar, Please

SCI 5.b. Students know organ systems function because of the contributions of individual organs, tissues, and cells. The failure of any part can affect the entire system.

Living things are made of carbon compounds called organic compounds. Many organic compounds are long molecules called polymers that consist of small, repeating units. Starch is a polymer of sugar units. When you eat a piece of bread, your body breaks down the starch in the bread. Substances in your saliva split the starch polymers into shorter chains of sugar units. Digestion continues in your stomach and intestines until shorter chains are broken down into individual sugar molecules. Finally, sugar molecules combine with oxygen in the cells to produce carbon dioxide and water and release energy.

Materials

- test-tube rack
- 4 test tubes
- test-tube holder
- solution X
- solution Y
- starch indicator solution
- hot plate
- watch or clock
- 250-mL heat-resistant beaker
- 100-mL heat-resistant beaker
- thermometer
- salivary amylase
- sugar indicator solution

What You'll Investigate

In this activity, you will use indicators to test unknown solutions for starch and sugar using a substance found in saliva.

Procedure

WARNING: *Starch indicator solution and sugar indicator solutions are poisonous. Handle with care.*

Part 1—Starch and Sugar Indicators

1. In the test tubes in front of you are two solutions. (Do not mix these.) You also have two bottles of liquids that are indicators. One is an indicator for starch. The other is for sugar. How could you tell which tubes have a starch solution? How could you tell which have a sugar solution? (The sugar indicator only works if the sugar is hot

enough. You need a hot-water bath prepared in a 250-mL beaker.)

2. Experiment with the solutions and indicators for a few minutes.

3. Choose some foods that are liquids or can be put into a liquid solution and write a hypothesis stating which will test as starch and which as sugar.

4. Design an experiment to investigate if foods you chose are starches, sugars, or neither.

5. Test your hypothesis and record your observations in **Table 1**.

6. Now that you know which liquids are starch, use an enzyme to see if you can break down the starch.

Part 2—Breakdown of Starch

1. Look at **Table 2** in Part 2.

2. Prepare a warm water bath in a 250-mL beaker. Make a mixture of warm and cool water to fill the beaker halfway. Use the thermometer to determine the temperature of the water. Add small amounts of warm or cool water using the 100-mL beaker until the temperature reaches 35°C to 40°C.

3. Use the test tube labeled *A* from Part 1. Fill it about a quarter full with salivary amylase.

4. Use the starch solution that you identified in Part 1. Add 15 drops of the starch solution you identified in Part 1 to the salivary amylase in the test tube. Shake the tube to mix the two liquids. Note the time. Place the

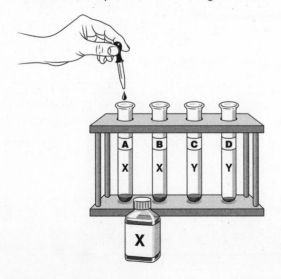

Inquiry Activity 5 (continued)

tube in the warm-water bath. See the following figure.

5. After 5 min, pour two small and equal portions of the liquid in tube A into tubes B and C. Do not use all the liquid from tube A.

6. Using the procedures in Part 1, place tube C in the boiling-water bath. Test the liquid in tube B for the presence of starch with the starch indicator solution. Record your observations of color changes in **Table 2**. Continue to time the reaction in tube A.

7. Leave tube A in the warm water bath. Add warm or cool water to the bath to adjust the bath temperature to 35°C to 40°C.

8. Rinse tubes B and C with water.

9. After another 5 min, repeat steps 4–6. If time allows, repeat these steps three times. Record your observations in **Table 2**.

Data and Observations

Part 1—Starch and Sugar Indicators Table 1

Tube	Unknown solution	Indicator solution	Color change	Starch (X)	Sugar (X)
A	X	starch			
B	X	sugar			
C	Y	starch			
D	Y	sugar			

Part 2—Breakdown of Starch Table 2

Time (min)	Color changes	
	Starch indicator–tube B	Sugar indicator–tube C
5		
10		
15		

Conclude and Apply

1. What happened to the starch solution when added to salivary amylase? How do you know this?

_____

_____

2. Why is a water bath at a temperature between 35°C and 40°C used in this experiment?

_____

Going Further

Draw a diagram showing the role of carbohydrates in photosynthesis.

Designing a Classification System

What's the difference between a butterfly and an elephant? The answer may seem obvious when talking about these two animals, but what would you say if someone asked you the difference between a butterfly and a moth? Being able to distinguish between different types of animals and plants is important to the scientists who study them. It allows them to organize information about each type of plant or animal in an efficient way. It ensures that each organism has its own distinct scientific name. For example, the great blue heron (*Ardea herodias*) and the blue jay (*Cyanocitta crestata*) would not be confused by a scientist because the scientific name is used. Scientific classification is based on categories.

Materials

Animals and plants that fall into similar categories are grouped together.

- pictures of animals
- scissors
- 15 small index cards
- tape or glue
- pencil

What You'll Investigate

In this activity, you will work with a partner to create your own animal classification system.

Procedure

1. Discuss with your lab partner your options for classifying the animals pictured. Decide which characteristics and how many characteristics you will assign to each animal. How many major characteristics will you have? How many minor characteristics?
2. Cut out the pictures of each animal given to you by your teacher. Glue one animal picture to the top of each index card.
3. Write the characteristics of each animal on the index cards, putting the major characteristics first.
4. Group the cards by category. Those animals with the most characteristics in common should be grouped together.
5. After you have finished your cards, on a separate sheet of paper, write down the letters of the animals that fall into the same main category.
6. Share your classification groups with other students.

 SCI 3.d. Students know how to construct a simple branching diagram to classify living groups of organisms by shared derived characteristics and how to expand the diagram to include fossil organisms.

Inquiry Activity 6 (continued)

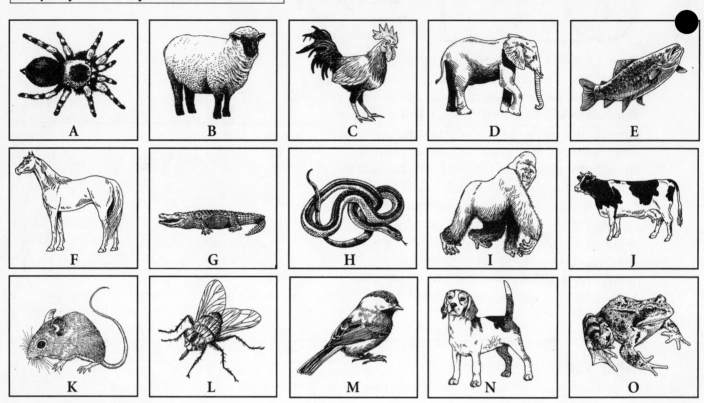

A   B   C   D   E

F   G   H   I   J

K   L   M   N   O

Conclude and Apply

1. How many classification groups did you create?

_____

2. Which animals were the most difficult to categorize? Why?

_____

3. Which animals did you need to know more about in order to categorize them correctly? Why?

_____

4. How was your classification system similar to that of other students? How was it different?

_____

_____

5. Of all the systems you observed, which do you think was the most efficient? Why?

_____

_____

Going Further

Scientific classification sometimes changes as new discoveries are made. Do research to find out how the classification of some dinosaurs has changed in the past 25 years.

LAB 7 Inquiry Activity

Growth Rings as Indicators of Climate

Trees are plants with woody stems called trunks. As shown in **Figure 1,** three types of vascular tissue—xylem, cambium, and phloem—make up the stem of a tree. Of these three tissues, xylem—the tissue that carries water and minerals up from the roots—takes up the most space.

If a tree is cut across its stem, a series of rings formed from alternating bands of lighter colored and darker colored wood can be seen. These rings are called growth rings, because each ring represents one year in the growth of the tree. Each growth ring is made up of both a dark and a light area.

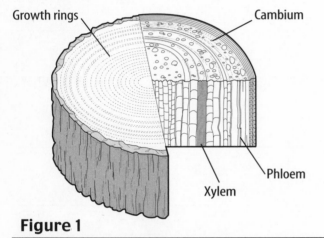

Growth rings — Cambium — Phloem — Xylem

Figure 1

Materials
- metric ruler

Growth rings result from differences in the rate at which xylem is produced at different times of the year. For example, spring wood forms from xylem cells that are large and wide. These xylem cells are made mostly during the spring when growing conditions, such as plentiful water, are favorable. When conditions become drier, summer wood is formed from xylem cells that are narrower and have thicker walls than the xylem that forms spring wood. Summer wood carries less water than spring wood.

Trees grow the most when environmental conditions, such as rainfall and temperature, are the most favorable. The size of the growth rings provide clues about the climate conditions of an area over time. During years when plenty of water is available, growth rings are wide. During dry periods, growth rings are narrower.

What You'll Investigate
In this activity, you will determine the age and growth patterns of trees based on the number and size of rings in the cross-sections shown in **Figures 2, 3,** and **4.**

Procedure
1. Examine the growth rings from living trees or those on the following page. Think of ways you could compare the ages of the trees and the type of weather that occurred while they were growing.

2. Determine what tools you will use for your exploration.
3. Decide on a procedure to follow with your partner to complete your study.
4. Communicate your findings to your class. Compare your responses.

SCI 5.a. Students know plants and animals have levels of organization for structure and function, including cells, tissues, organs, organ systems, and the whole organism.

Inquiry Activity 7 (continued)

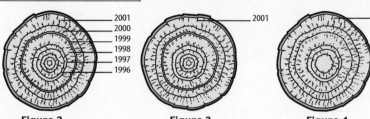

Figure 2   Figure 3   Figure 4

Data and Observations

Tree	# of rings	Age of tree	Total width (in cm)	Widest ring/ year	Narrowest ring/ year

Conclude and Apply

1. What is the relationship between the number of rings in a tree's trunk and the age of the tree?

   _____

   _____

2. In which year do you think the area around the tree in **Figure 2** received the most rainfall? Why?

   _____

   _____

3. In which year did the tree in **Figure 3** receive the most water? Explain.

   _____

   _____

4. In which year did the tree in **Figure 4** receive the least water? Explain.

   _____

   _____

5. The trees represented by **Figures 2, 3,** and **4** grew in different parts of the United States. In which of these areas do you think conditions were most suited to growth? Why?

   _____

   _____

Going Further

Do research to find out how dendrochronology (dating past events by looking at tree rings) is used to determine the age of wooden artifacts discovered by archaeologists.

Forensics Activities

Fleet Feet

The Problem

Mr. and Mrs. G returned home from a movie late Saturday night and found a police cruiser at their home. The alarm from their home security system had gone off, apparently as a result of a break-in. The police found that a basement window had been broken, but no items were missing.

The couple recently had some landscaping work done in the area of the break-in. The lawn outside the window had been reseeded, and the soil was kept damp from the sprinkler system.

Investigators found shoe prints leading up to the window and a path of shoe prints leading away from the window. Investigators hypothesize that the robber entered the house through the window, but quickly left the scene after triggering the alarm system.

In this lab, you will examine shoe prints taken from the crime scene in order to create a preliminary profile of the suspect.

Background

Prints Shoe prints can be useful evidence collected at a crime scene. Prints left behind in soft sediment or in a powdery substance can provide clues about a suspect's physical makeup.

A person's shoe size, weight, and height can be estimated from shoe prints left in soft material. Have you ever looked at the bottom of your shoes or sneakers and noticed that some areas are more worn than others? These wear patterns can also provide clues about a person's size and walking stride.

Material

❑ metric ruler

Procedure

1. Examine the crime scene shoe prints, and measure the following:

   • mean, or average, length and width of the prints; measure width at widest part of print

   • mean, or average, depth of the prints; measure depth at deepest part of print

   • mean, or average, distance between prints; measure distance from toe part of print to heel part of next print

   Measurements will vary somewhat from print to print, so take an average of your measurements to account for this.

Record your information in **Table 1**.

Do not disturb the footprints when taking your measurements; other groups will need to examine the same set of footprints to collect their data.

2. Make a sketch of the shoe print in **Table 2**. Be sure to include any wear patterns.

3. Have a volunteer from your group sprint the length of the soil track. Take footprint measurements as you did in step 2. Record your results in **Table 1**, then make a sketch of the print in **Table 2**.

 SCI 7.c. Communicate the logical connection among hypotheses, science concepts, tests conducted, data collected, and conclusions drawn from the scientific evidence.

Forensics Activity 1 (continued)

4. Use the rake to fill in the footprints and level the soil.

5. Repeat steps 3 and 4 for each volunteer in your group. Record your results in **Table 1**, then make a sketch of each print in **Table 2**.

6. Clean up the area as instructed by your teacher, then answer the questions that follow.

Data and Observations

Table 1

	Suspect	Volunteer 1	Volunteer 2	Volunteer 3	Volunteer 4
Average shoe print size (length and width in cm)					
Average shoe print depth (cm)					
Distance between shoe prints (m)					
Height of suspect					
Weight of suspect					
Shoe size of suspect					

Forensics Activity 1 (continued)

Table 2

	Shoe Pattern Sketch
Suspect	
Volunteer 1	
Volunteer 2	
Volunteer 3	
Volunteer 4	

Conclude and Apply

1. Examine each of the *distance between shoe prints* and *height* measurements. Do you notice a relationship between the two? Explain.

_____

_____

_____

_____

Forensics Activity 1 (continued)

2. Describe how the shoe prints of a person sprinting would compare with the shoe prints of a person walking. Include *average shoe print depth* and *distance between shoe prints* in your description.

_____

_____

_____

_____

3. Examine each of the *average shoe print depth* and *weight* measurements. Do you notice a relationship between the two? Explain.

_____

_____

_____

_____

4. Describe any differences between the shoe prints of the males and the shoe prints of the females in your group.

_____

_____

_____

Analyze and Conclude

5. Describe the person that the police should be looking for in connection to this crime.

_____

_____

_____

_____

6. Describe at least two other pieces of evidence that police should look for at the crime scene.

_____

_____

_____

_____

Trouble in Wildwood

LAB 2 Forensics Activity

The Problem

Three businesses in Wildwood have been robbed within the last week.
Police have gathered the following information:

- The Wildwood Convenience Store was robbed at 1 A.M. on Friday, October 14.
  The robber entered the store and demanded all the cash on hand. The robber
  made off with an unspecified amount of money but cut his finger in the process
  of destroying a nearby surveillance camera.

- The Night Owl Restaurant was robbed at 12:50 A.M. on Monday, October 17.
  The robber entered the diner and handed a sealed envelope to the cashier,
  insisting that she read it. The note inside said the store was being held up, but
  no one would be hurt if all the cash was handed over immediately. The robber
  made a crucial mistake by accidentally leaving behind the envelope and note.

- The Wildwood Bowling Alley was robbed at 11:10 P.M. on Thursday, October 20.
  Once again, the robber demanded all the cash and left quickly. On the way out,
  however, the robber stumbled and fell while running down stairs. The bowling
  alley manager noticed that a piece of gum flew from the robber's mouth and
  landed on the carpet.

The police have rounded up three possible suspects, and they all have agreed
to give DNA samples. Your job is to analyze the DNA left at each crime scene
and then compare it to the DNA samples of the three suspects.

Background

DNA Fingerprints DNA fingerprinting is one
of the most significant developments in forensic
science since the introduction of traditional
fingerprinting. DNA results can provide powerful
evidence in court, but it is important to
understand that DNA matching is not 100 percent
reliable. DNA evidence usually represents just part
of all the evidence presented in a court case.

The DNA fingerprinting technique produces a
unique pattern of bands that can be used for
identification. This unique banding pattern
produced by fragments of your DNA is called
DNA fingerprinting. Unless you have an identical
twin, no one has the exact DNA fingerprint that
you have. Genetic markers can help identify the
differences between two DNA samples.

Scientists use polymerase chain reactions
(PCR) and gel electrophoresis to make a DNA
fingerprint. PCR allows scientists to make many
copies of a DNA segment without using living
cells. One particular segment can be copied from
a larger length of DNA. The DNA fragments
then are separated by gel electrophoresis. In this
process, the molecules or portions of molecules
are separated by their length.

When used together, PCR and gel electrophoresis techniques allow law enforcement
officials to gather the smallest amount of evidence
at a crime scene. DNA gathered from blood, hair,
and saliva samples at a crime scene can then be
compared to a suspect's DNA fingerprint.

SCI 2.e. Students know DNA (deoxyribonucleic acid) is the genetic material of living organisms and is
located in the chromosomes of each cell.

Forensics Activity 2 (continued)

Everyday Materials

❏ colored pencils

Lab Materials

❏ ruler

❏ magnifying lens

❏ DNA samples from crime scenes

❏ DNA samples from suspects

Procedure

1. Your teacher will give you a printout that shows DNA samples from the three crime scenes, as well as DNA samples from the three suspects. Your teacher will also identify which DNA samples were found at each location, and which DNA samples belong to each suspect.

2. Take the printout and turn it so that the longest side of the page is facing you. Examine the convenience store sample.

Use a ruler and colored pencil to draw a line through each band (dark rectangular marks). Examine whether most of the bands align with most of the bands from Suspects A, B, or C.

3. Repeat step 2 for the restaurant sample. Use a different colored pencil.

4. Repeat step 2 for the bowling alley sample. Use a different colored pencil.

5. Answer the following questions.

Conclude and Apply

1. Why is DNA fingerprinting so effective in solving crimes like the ones described in this lab?

_____

_____

_____

_____

_____

Forensics Activity 2 (continued)

2. Describe how police obtained DNA samples from the convenience store, the restaurant, and the bowling alley.

_____

_____

_____

_____

_____

3. Suppose detectives learn that Suspect C has an identical twin. How will this change their investigation?

_____

_____

_____

4. Do you think the same person committed the robberies? Explain your reasoning.

_____

_____

_____

_____

Analyze and Conclude

5. Would you recommend that the police continue to question any of the suspects? If so, specify which suspect(s) should be questioned in each robbery. Keep in mind that most, but not all, of the DNA bands should align when there is a match between a location and a suspect.

_____

_____

_____

_____

_____

_____

Forensics Activity 2 (continued)

6. Considering only the DNA evidence from the printout, should the police consider releasing any of the suspects? Explain.

_____

_____

_____

_____

7. Do detectives need to gather more evidence in the cases? Explain.

_____

_____

_____

_____

8. Bar codes are widely used in stores. How is a bar code similar to a DNA fingerprint?

_____

_____

_____

_____

LAB 3 Forensics Activity

A Hairy Situation

The Problem

The nightshift supervisor of a local zoo is discovered locked up in an unused room. The supervisor is shaken but otherwise unharmed. When the police arrive, she explains that she was just about to begin feeding the animals when she was grabbed from behind and forced into the room by an unknown male attacker.

It is quickly discovered that an exotic Siberian tiger cub is missing from his cage. The police are searching for physical clues that the thief might have left behind. As part of the investigation, they plan to examine hairs found on the supervisor's jacket.

The supervisor has provided the following information:

- The coat was recently picked up from the dry cleaners. The plastic cover was not removed until she began work on the night of the incident.

- She has a cat at home.

- She has dark hair.

In this lab, you will be analyzing three different hair samples gathered from the coat of the victim. Your job will be to determine if any could have come from the thief.

Background

Hair Analysis Hair analysis can be used to rule out suspects or possible scenarios. Hair analysis can also be used to corroborate, or support, other physical evidence when it is consistent with the rest of the gathered evidence.

However, in terms of physical evidence, hair analysis is limited because it cannot prove with certainty that two hairs have come from the same person.

Hair Structure All hair has three main parts: the medulla, the cortex, and the cuticle. The medulla is the central core of a hair and is surrounded by the protein-rich cortex. This is the part of a hair that contains the pigment. The outer coating of a hair is called the cuticle and is formed of overlapping scales.

Think of a strand of hair as a pencil. The medulla is like the graphite inside the pencil. The cortex is like the wood surrounding the graphite, and the cuticle is like the paint on the outside of the pencil.

Examining Hairs The thickness of the cuticle can vary, and some species can have cuticles that contain pigments. Characteristics of the cuticle can be important in distinguishing between hairs of different species but are not often useful in distinguishing between different people. For example, a house cat belongs to the species *Felis silvestris catus*. This species has a thinner cuticle compared to humans, or *Homo sapiens*. The medulla can vary in thickness, continuity, and transparency. The cortex varies in thickness, texture, and color.

Copyright © by Glencoe/McGraw-Hill, a division of The McGraw-Hill Companies, Inc.

SCI 7.e. Communicate the steps and results from an investigation in written reports and oral presentations. Also covers **SCI 5.a.**

Forensics Activity 3 (continued)

Everyday Materials

❏ water

Lab Materials

❏ separate envelopes with
several hair strands in each

❏ microscope

❏ microscope slide

❏ cover slips

❏ dropper

❏ slides of cat hair and
human hair

Safety

- Always wear safety goggles and a lab apron.
- Wash your hands thoroughly after each lab.

Procedure

1. Put on your lab apron and safety goggles, and wear them for the entire experiment.

2. Examine Slide 1 (cat hair) under the microscope using high power, then complete **Table 1** in the *Data and Observations* section.

3. Repeat step 2 for Slide 2 (human male hair) and Slide 3 (human female hair).

4. Make a sketch of each slide in the *Data and Observations* section using your information from **Table 1**. Be sure to label your sketches.

5. Obtain the three envelopes of hair samples from your teacher. These are the three different samples that were found on the supervisor's jacket.

6. Label a slide for each envelope; use the letter your teacher has written on the envelope.

7. Open Envelope A. Remove one of the hairs. Prepare a wet-mount slide of the hair using your labeled slides.

8. Examine the slide under the microscope using high power. Complete **Table 2.**

9. Repeat steps 7 and 8 for Envelopes B and C.

10. Make a sketch of each slide in the *Data and Observations* section using your information from **Table 2.** Pay special attention to the cuticle thickness in each sketch. Be sure to label your sketches.

Data and Observations

Table 1

	Slide 1 (Cat Hair)	Slide 2 (Human Male)	Slide 3 (Human Female)
Medulla present?			
Cortex present?			
Cuticle present?			
Color			

Forensics Activity 3 (continued)

Sketch

Slide 1	Slide 2	Slide 3

Table 2

	Envelope A	Envelope B	Envelope C
Medulla present?			
Cortex present?			
Cuticle present?			
Color			

Sketch

Envelope A	Envelope B	Envelope C

Forensics Activity 3 (continued)

Conclude and Apply

1. Review your observations from **Table 1.** Describe any characteristics the hair samples have in common.

_____

_____

_____

_____

_____

2. Review your observations from **Table 1.** Describe any differences in the hair samples.

_____

_____

_____

_____

_____

3. Review your observations from **Table 2** (samples from the jacket). Describe any characteristics the hair samples have in common.

_____

_____

_____

_____

_____

4. Review your observations from **Table 2.** Describe any differences in the hair samples.

_____

_____

_____

_____

_____

Copyright © by Glencoe/McGraw-Hill, a division of The McGraw-Hill Companies, Inc.

Forensics Activity 3 (continued)

5. Do the slide samples from **Table 1** appear to match any of the envelope samples from **Table 2**? If so, describe the matches.

_____

_____

_____

_____

_____

Analyze and Conclude

6. Attempt to match the three envelope samples to the supervisor, her pet, and the thief. Explain your reasoning.

_____

_____

_____

_____

_____

7. In question 6, were you able to match one of the envelope samples to the potential thief? If so, what can you say about the suspect's appearance from the hair samples alone?

_____

_____

_____

8. How useful would your hair analysis be in court? Explain your answer.

_____

_____

_____

LAB
4 Forensics Activity

The Missing Tenant

The Problem

Police are called to an apartment building. The landlord had gone to apartment 4D to collect the monthly rent and found the door slightly open. The landlord knocked and called out several times, but no one answered. She entered the apartment to make sure everything was okay. When the landlord looked in the kitchen, she found what appeared to be blood on the floor. She immediately left the apartment and called the police, concerned that her tenant might be injured.

Your job is to determine if the stains are blood. If this is the case, a more detailed analysis can then be made.

Background

Catalase Have you ever added hydrogen peroxide to a cut? If so, you probably noticed that the cut bubbles and fizzes. This happens because blood contains an enzyme called catalase. Catalase breaks down hydrogen peroxide into water and oxygen. When this reaction occurs, the oxygen is released as bubbles. Hydrogen peroxide is toxic to living cells, so catalase performs an important function by breaking it down. Plants and some bacteria also contain catalase.

Phenolphthalein Test While hydrogen peroxide is effective in detecting the presence of blood, phenolphthalein is a chemical that is most often used for this purpose at actual crime scenes. This test relies on peroxidase enzymes found in blood to react with phenolphthalein. If a drop of phenolphthalein solution is placed on a bloodstain, it will turn white to light pink. If phenolphthalein solution is added to a red stain that is not blood, the stain will remain dark red or purple.

Everyday Materials

❑ cotton balls

❑ six samples from crime scene

❑ fresh berries

❑ red paint

❑ fresh tomato sauce

❑ cooked tomato sauce

Lab Materials

❑ simulated blood sample

❑ phenolphthalein solution

❑ eye droppers

Safety

- Always wear safety goggles and a lab apron.
- Wash your hands thoroughly after each lab activity.
- Never eat or drink anything in the lab.

Procedure

1. Put on your lab apron and eye goggles, and wear them for the entire experiment.

2. Examine the table on the next page. It includes a list of red substances that were found inside apartment 4D. Make a prediction as to whether or not each substance will test positive or negative for the presence of peroxidase enzymes. Explain your reasoning.

SCI 5.b. Students know organ systems function because of the contributions of individual organs, tissues, and cells. The failure of any part can affect the entire system.

Forensics Activity 4 (continued)

3. Obtain samples of each substance in the table. Transfer a small amount of each substance to a clean cotton ball. Place one drop of phenolphthalein on the substance, and record your findings in the table.

4. Obtain the six samples from the crime scene. Use the phenolphthalein solution on the samples. Record your results in the table.

5. Dispose of the materials as instructed by your teacher, then answer the questions that follow.

Data and Observations

Substance	Prediction: Reacts with Phenolphthalein?	Why?	Actual Result
Blood			
Red paint			
Fresh tomato sauce			
Heated tomato sauce			
Fresh red berries			

Forensics Activity 4 (continued)

Conclude and Apply

1. Briefly describe how hydrogen peroxide and phenolphthalein are used to detect the presence of blood.

_____

_____

_____

_____

_____

2. Why do you think phenolphthalein rather than hydrogen peroxide is used to detect blood at crime scenes?

_____

_____

_____

_____

_____

3. Would the test for peroxidase enzymes work on a very small sample of blood? Explain.

_____

_____

_____

_____

_____

Forensics Activity 4 (continued)

Analyze and Conclude

4. Based on your findings, could some of the stains at the scene possibly be the tenant's blood? Explain.

_____

_____

_____

_____

_____

5. If you answered *yes* to question 4, what other tests might investigators run on the bloodstains?

_____

_____

_____

_____

_____

6. Do you think investigators could gather information from the pattern and shape of the blood drops at the scene? Explain.

_____

_____

_____

_____

_____

LAB

5 Forensics Activity

Break-in at the Grand Hotel

The Problem

The police are called to the Grand Hotel. It appears that a robbery took place within the last few hours. One of the customers returned to his room to find the door open and the room ransacked. Jewelry, cash, and other valuable items were stolen.

Police took the fingerprints of the customer and all the hotel staff who had access to the room. The police also removed several items that might provide fingerprint evidence. These items include a drinking glass, a hairbrush, and a wooden jewelry box.

There are three suspects in the case. Suspect A was recently fired from the Grand Hotel. Suspect B was a protester who stood outside the hotel regularly, protesting that fur coats are unnecessary and result in animal cruelty. Suspect C is an assistant who travels with the victim. Your job is to examine fingerprints taken from the items to see if police should further pursue any of the three suspects.

Background

Fingerprints There are three main types of fingerprints: the whorl, the arch, and the loop.

Whorl patterns (**Figure 1**) are found in 35 percent of the population. These patterns have at least one ridge that makes a complete circuit, creating a spiral or oval in the center of the print.

Figure 1

Arch patterns (**Figure 2**) are found in approximately 5 percent of the population. These patterns have lines that start at one side of the print and then move toward the center of the print. The lines peak, then sweep down on the other side.

Figure 2

Loop patterns (**Figure 3**) are found in approximately 60 percent of the population. These patterns have lines that start at one side of the print, curve again, and then exit on the same side that they began.

Figure 3

Crime Scenes Fingerprints can be left at a crime scene in three different ways.

- Visible prints can be seen by the naked eye. These are made when fingers touch a surface after the ridges have been in contact with material such as paint, blood, ink, or grease.

- Latent prints are left behind when the perspiration on a person's skin comes in contact with a surface and makes an invisible impression on it.

- Plastic prints are impressions left in a soft material such as dust, soap, wax, or putty.

SCI 3.a. Students know both genetic variation and environmental factors are causes of evolution and diversity of organisms.

Forensics Activity 5 (continued)

Everyday Materials

❏ cocoa powder

❏ soap

❏ water

❏ clear tape wide enough to include a fingerprint

❏ pencils

❏ paper

Lab Materials

❏ magnifying lens

❏ ink pad

❏ microscope slides

❏ fine paint brushes

❏ latex gloves

❏ collection of fingerprints on file with law enforcement

Safety

- Always use safety goggles and a lab apron.
- Wash your hands thoroughly after each lab activity.

Procedure

1. Put on your lab apron and safety goggles, and wear them for the entire experiment.

2. In this step, you will be taking your own fingerprint. On a separate sheet of paper, make a 2.5 cm × 2.5 cm square. Use a pencil to fill in the square; be sure to completely cover the area. Place your right thumb on the left of the square, then firmly roll your thumb to the right.

3. Place a strip of clear tape over your thumb, and gently remove the tape. Place the tape in the appropriate box in **Table 1** below. You might need to trim the edges of the tape so that it fits neatly in the box.

4. Repeat step 2 with each of your fingers on your right hand. Label each print as an *arch*, *loop*, or *whorl* in the box below the print.

5. Use an ink pad to take the fingerprint of the right index finger of each member of your group, including yourself. Tightly grasp the person's right hand. Roll the finger from left to right on the surface of the ink pad.

6. Place the print in **Table 2** by placing the left side of the finger on the paper and rolling the finger to the right. Then lift the person's finger straight up to avoid smearing. Label each box with the person's name. Wash your hands with soap and water before proceeding.

7. Each member of your group will now create a latent print on a microscope slide. Rub your right index finger on the side of your nose, and then press down gently on the slide.

8. Your group should then collect all the slides and redistribute them. You should put on latex gloves to avoid smearing the slides.

9. Dust for the print by using the cocoa powder and a small paintbrush. Dip the brush into the cocoa powder. Lightly brush the powder over the print. Try to avoid smearing the print.

10. Once a print is visible, lift it by carefully placing a piece of clear tape over it. Press down gently on the tape to lift the print, then place the tape in the box in **Table 3**. Trim the excess tape, if necessary, before placing it in the box. Include the name of the person and the type of fingerprint pattern in the boxes below.

11. Using one of the methods practiced above, lift a print from each of the three items from the crime scene. Record the information in **Table 4**.

12. Obtain a database of fingerprints from your teacher. See if you can match the suspect's fingerprint with one from the database.

13. Clean up your work area as instructed by your teacher.

Copyright © by Glencoe/McGraw-Hill, a division of The McGraw-Hill Companies, Inc.

Forensics Activity 5 (continued)

Data and Observations

Table 1

Thumb	Index	Middle	Ring	Pinkie

Table 2

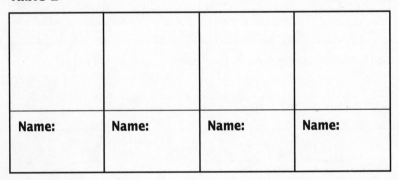

Name:	Name:	Name:	Name:

Table 3

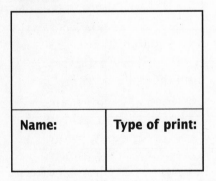

Name:	Type of print:

Table 4

Glass	Hairbrush	Jewelry Box

Forensics Activity 5 (continued)

Conclude and Apply

1. Which of the three types of fingerprint patterns do you have? Explain how you were able to identify your fingerprint type.

_____

_____

_____

2. Why is the use of clear tape so effective in this lab?

_____

_____

_____

3. Why did you have to rub your finger on the side of your nose before making the latent print?

_____

_____

_____

4. Why is a fine powder such as cocoa effective in lifting prints?

_____

_____

_____

5. Why did you have to put on latex gloves before examining the items from the crime scene?

_____

_____

_____

Forensics Activity 5 (continued)

Analyze and Conclude

6. Do you have a suspect in the robbery? Explain your answer.

_____

_____

_____

_____

7. How can you be sure that it was not another person whose fingerprints were not in the database? Explain your answer.

_____

_____

_____

_____

8. If you answered *yes* to question 6, what do you think would be the next logical step in the investigation process?

_____

_____

_____

_____

Probeware Activities

Getting Started with Probeware

The following instructions will guide you through the setup process for the data collection unit and the graphing calculator. The activities are compatible with either the CBL 2 or the LabPro unit. Each activity was written for use with TI-73 or TI-83 Plus graphing calculators. These activities can be adapted for use with other graphing calculators or other data collection units, if desired.

Connecting a Graphing Calculator to the CBL 2 or LabPro Unit

1. Insert batteries into the CBL 2 or LabPro unit and graphing calculator.

2. The cradle is an optional accessory that conveniently connects the two units. Slide the back of the cradle onto the front of the CBL 2 or LabPro unit until it clicks into place.

3. Insert the upper end of the calculator into the cradle and press down on the lower end until it locks into place.

4. Connect the CBL 2 or LabPro unit to the graphing calculator using the unit-to-unit link cable. Plug the cable into the I/O port at the end of the CBL 2 or LabPro unit and the other end into the I/O port at the end of the calculator. Make sure that the unit-to-unit link cable is securely in place.

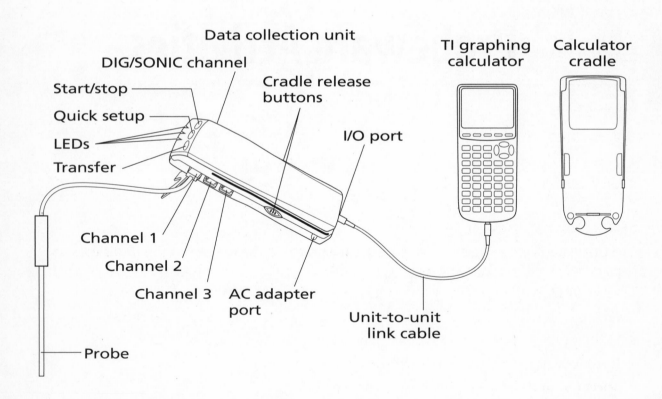

Resetting the Calculator Memory

It is recommended that the memory of the calculator be cleared before the DataMate data collection program is transferred.

1. Press [2nd] [MEM].

2. Select **Reset.**

3. Select **ALL RAM...**

4. Select **Reset.** The calculator screen will display **RAM cleared.**

Transferring DataMate to the Calculator

The DataMate program is stored on the CBL 2 or LabPro unit and is transferred to the graphing calculator for use. Once DataMate is transferred to the graphing calculator, it will remain there until the calculator memory is reset using the instructions above.

1. For the TI-73, press [APPS]. Select **Link...**

   For the TI-83 Plus, press [2nd] [**LINK**].

2. Use the right arrow to highlight **RECEIVE.** Press [ENTER].

3. The screen will display **Waiting...** Press the large **TRANSFER** key found on the upper left-hand side of the CBL 2 or LabPro unit. When the transfer is complete, the screen will display the transferred programs followed by the word **Done.**

4. Press [2nd] [**QUIT**].

Starting DataMate

When you are ready to collect data, use the following instructions to start DataMate.

For the TI-73:

1. Press [PRGM].

2. Select **DataMate.**

3. Press [ENTER].

For the TI-83 Plus:

1. Press [APPS].

2. Select **DataMate.**

Setting up Probes Manually

The CBL 2 and LabPro unit should recognize the probe attached automatically. If this does not happen, follow these instructions.

1. Select **SETUP** from the DataMate main screen.

2. Press [ENTER] to select channel 1, or select the channel where the probe is inserted.

3. Select the correct sensor number from the SELECT SENSOR menu.

4. If requested, select the type of probe used.

5. Select **OK** to return to the DataMate main screen.

Using the TI-73 Graphing Calculator to Create a Histogram

A histogram is a graph that shows data divided into equal ranges and the number of data points that fall into each range. The following instructions explain how to make a histogram for the heart rate data in *Exercise and Heart Rate*.

1. **Resetting Calculator Memory** Turn on your graphing calculator and press `2nd` [MEM]. Select **Clr All Lists.** Press `ENTER`.

2. **Creating and Entering Data Into Lists** Press `LIST` to access an empty data table. Name your lists before entering data. Scroll up to the title bar (the "top shelf") and over to the first empty list beyond L6 (lists L1–L6 cannot be renamed). Press `2nd` [TEXT]. Scroll to the desired letters, pressing `ENTER` after each. Choose a title of 5 or fewer letters. Then scroll down to **DONE.** Press `ENTER` twice to title your new list. Repeat for the other two variables. Enter your class data in all three lists.

3. **Setting up Graphs** Press `2nd` [PLOT]. Select **Plot 1** by pressing `ENTER`. Use the arrow keys and `ENTER` to turn the plot on and to select the sixth graph icon, a histogram. For the Xlist, press `2nd` `LIST` and scroll down to find the resting heart rate list. Press `ENTER` twice. Ignore Freq.

  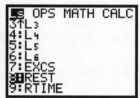 

4. Repeat **Step 3** to set up Plot 2 and Plot 3, but do not turn them ON yet. The Xlists will be your exercise heart rate and recovery time lists.

5. **Plotting Data** Press `ZOOM`. Then select **ZoomStat** to see your first histogram for resting heart rate. Use the `TRACE` and arrow keys to find the heart rate range that occurred in the class most often and the number of students that were in this range.

6. Press `2nd` [PLOT] to turn off Plot 1, and turn on Plot 2. Repeat step 5 for Plot 3 to see the class histogram for exercise heart rate and recovery time.

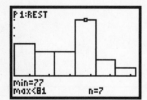 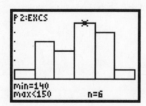 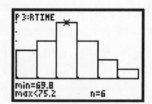

Using the TI-83 Plus Graphing Calculator to Create a Histogram

1. **Resetting Calculator Memory** Turn on your graphing calculator and press [2nd] [MEM]. Select **Clr All Lists.** Press [ENTER].

2. **Creating and Entering Data into Lists** Name your lists before entering data. Press [STAT] and select **Edit.** Scroll up to the title bar (the "top shelf") and over to the first empty list beyond L6 (lists L1–L6 cannot be renamed). The highlighted "A" in the upper corner indicates that you are already in locked-alpha mode. Find and press the desired letters on the keypad. Press [ENTER] to title your new list for the resting heart rate data. Repeat for exercise heart rate and recovery time. Choose abbreviations that make sense to you—the names are limited to five letters. Enter all data.

  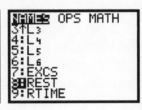

3. **Setting up Graphs** Set up your calculator for graphing your data. Press [2nd] [**STAT PLOT**]. Select **Plot 1** by pressing [ENTER]. Use the arrow keys and [ENTER] to turn the plot on and select the third graph icon, a histogram. For the Xlist, press [2nd] [LIST] and scroll down to find your resting heart rate list. Press [ENTER] twice. Leave Freq. at 1.

4. Repeat **Step 3** to set up Plot 2 and then Plot 3, but do not turn Plot 2 and Plot 3 ON yet. The Xlists will be your exercise heart rate and recovery time lists.

5. **Plotting Data** Press [ZOOM]. Then select **ZoomStat** to see the first histogram, for resting heart rate. Use the [TRACE] and arrow keys to find the heart rate range that occurred in the class most often and the number of students that were in this range.

6. Press [2nd] [STAT] [**PLOT**] to turn off Plot 1, and turn on Plot 2. Press [ZOOM]. Then select **ZoomStat** again to see the class histogram for exercise heart rate. Then turn off Plot 2 and turn on Plot 3 to see the class histogram for recovery time.

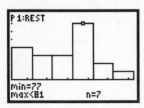 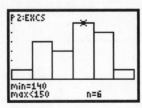 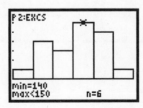

Using the TI-73 Graphing Calculator to Create a Box Plot and Display Statistics

Note: If you have already used the calculator to make histograms, skip to step #4.

1. **Resetting Calculator Memory** Turn on your graphing calculator and press `2nd` [**MEM**]. Select **Clr All Lists.** Press `ENTER`.

2. Press `LIST` to access an empty data table. Name your lists before entering data. Scroll up to the title bar (the "top shelf") and over to the first empty list beyond L6 (lists L1–L6 cannot be renamed). Press `2nd` [**TEXT**]. Use the arrow keys to select the desired letters, pressing `ENTER` after each. List names are limited to five letters. Go to **DONE** when you are finished entering the name. Press `ENTER` twice to title your new list for the resting heart rate data.

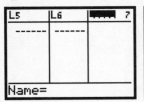  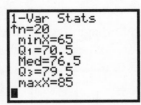

3. Repeat for the other two variables, choosing abbreviations for exercise heart rate and recovery time with 5 or fewer letters. Enter your class data in all three lists.

4. Order the data in your lists. Press `2nd` [**STAT**]. Use the right arrow key to select **OPS.** Select the default, **Sort A,** by pressing `ENTER`. The blinking cursor is a signal to insert your list names. Press `2nd` `LIST` and scroll down to select your first list. Then enter a comma. Repeat to select the second and third data lists. The commas will keep the lists separated so you can later investigate any relationship between variables. Press `ENTER`. With data sorted (in ascending order), you can easily determine the minimum, maximum, mode, and median.

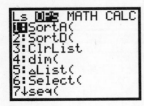 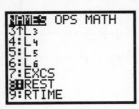 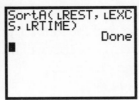 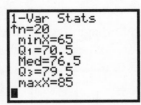

5. For statistical analysis, access the one-variable statistics for each list. Press `2nd` [**STAT**]. Use the right arrow key to select **CALC.** Select the default, **1–Var Stats.** Press `ENTER`. Press `2nd` `LIST` to retrieve one of your lists. Press `ENTER`. The mean (x) is the first entry. Scroll down to find the minimum (minX), median (Med), and maximum (maxX).

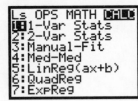 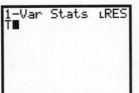 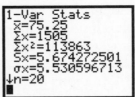 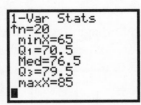

6. Set up your calculator for graphing your data. Press `2nd` **[PLOT]**. Select the default, **Plot 1,** by pressing `ENTER`. Use the arrow keys and `ENTER` to turn the plot on and select the seventh graph icon, a standard box plot. For the Xlist, press `2nd` `LIST` and scroll down to find your resting heart rate list. Press `ENTER` twice. Leave Freq. at 1.

  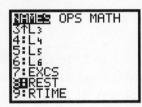 

7. Repeat **Step 5** to set up and turn on Plot 2 and then Plot 3. The Xlists will be your exercise heart rate and recovery time lists. Because the data for all three lists is in the same range (about 60–160), all three box plots can be viewed on the calculator screen simultaneously. Remember that the first two plots are heart rates measured in beats per minute while the last plot, recovery time, is measured in seconds.

8. Press `ZOOM`. Select **ZoomStat** to see all three box plots, for resting heart rate. Using the `TRACE` and arrow keys find the median exercise heart rate. The left and right arrows will give you the minimum, maximum, median, and quartiles. The up and down arrows allow you to trace the three plots—Plot 1 is at the top of the screen. You also can see that the maximum the minimum heart rates and recovery times.

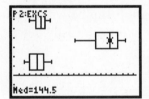 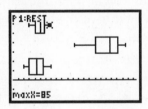 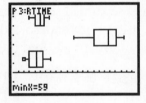

Using the TI-83 Plus Graphing Calculator to Box Plot and Display Statistics

Note: If you have already used the calculator to make histograms, skip to step #3.

1. **Resetting Calculator Memory** Turn on your graphing calculator and press 2nd [MEM]. Select **Clr All Lists.** Press ENTER.

2. Name your lists. Press STAT and select **Edit.** Scroll up to the title bar (the "top shelf") and over to the first empty list beyond L6 (lists L1–L6 cannot be renamed). The highlighted "A" in the upper corner indicates that you are already in locked-alpha mode. Find and press the desired letters. Press ENTER to title your new list for the resting heart rate data. Repeat for the other two variables, exercise heart rate and recovery time. Choose abbreviations that make sense to you— list names are limited to five letters. Then enter all data.

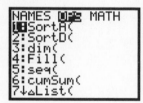

3. Order the data in your lists. Press 2nd LIST and use the right arrow key to select **OPS.** Select the default, **Sort A,** by pressing ENTER. The blinking cursor is a signal to insert your list names. Press 2nd LIST and scroll down to select your first list. Then enter a comma. Repeat to select the second and third data lists. Then put a right parentheses ")" after the lists. The commas will keep the lists separated so you can later investigate any relationship between variables if you like. Press ENTER. With data sorted (in ascending order here) you can easily determine the minimum, maximum, mode, and median.

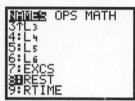

4. For statistical analysis, access the one-variable statistics for each list. Press STAT and arrow right to **CALC.** Select the default, **1-Var Stats.** Press ENTER. Press 2nd LIST and scroll down to retrieve one of your lists. Press ENTER twice. The mean (x) is the first entry, then scroll down to find the minimum (minX), median (Med), and maximum (maxX).

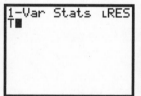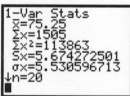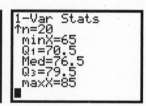

5. Set up your calculator for graphing your data. Press ⌈ 2nd ⌉ **[STAT PLOT].** Select the default, **Plot 1,** by pressing ⌈ENTER⌉. Use the arrow and ⌈ENTER⌉ keys to turn the plot on and select the fifth graph icon, a standard box plot. For the Xlist, press ⌈ 2nd ⌉ ⌈ LIST ⌉ and scroll down to find your resting heart rate list. Press ⌈ENTER⌉ twice. Leave Freq at 1.

  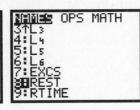 

6. Repeat **Step 5** to set up and turn on Plot 2 and Plot 3. The Xlists will be your exercise heart rate and recovery time lists. Because the data for all three lists is in the same range (about 60–160), all three box plots can be viewed on the calculator screen simultaneously. Remember that the first two plots are heart rates measured in beats per minute while the last plot, recovery time, is measured in seconds.

7. Press ⌈ZOOM⌉ and select **ZoomStat** to see all three box plots for resting heart rate. Using the ⌈TRACE⌉ and arrow keys, find the median exercise heart rate. The left and right arrows will give you the minimum, maximum, median, and quartiles. The up and down arrows allow you to trace the three plots—Plot 1 is at the top of the screen. You can find the maximum and minimum heart rates and recovery times.

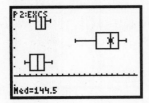 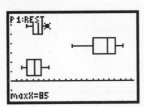 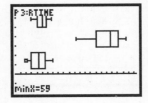

Using the TI-73 Graphing Calculator to Create a Circle Graph

1. **Resetting Calculator Memory** Turn on your graphing calculator and press ⌈2nd⌉ [MEM]. Select **ClrAllLists.** Press ⌈ENTER⌉.

2. Press ⌈LIST⌉ to access an empty data table. Name your lists before entering data. Scroll up to the title bar (the "top shelf") and over to the first empty list beyond L6 (lists L1–L6 cannot be renamed). Press ⌈2nd⌉ [TEXT]. Use the arrow keys to select the desired letters, pressing ⌈ENTER⌉ after each. Your title can only have 5 or fewer letters. Select **DONE** when you are finished. Press ⌈ENTER⌉ twice to title your new list for the plant type data at Site A. Make three more lists, naming them TOTA, PLNTB, and TOTB.

3. Enter your plant data. Because this data is "categorical" instead of numerical, you must use quotation marks around the first entry only. Place your cursor at the first entry for the list named PLNTA. Press ⌈2nd⌉ [TEXT] and scroll first to the quotes and press ⌈ENTER⌉. Choose your letters, ending with quotes. Notice that a small "c" appears next to the title of a categorical list. Enter the rest of your plant types—you do not need quotes for the rest. Enter the total number of each plant in the next list. Enter data for Site B as well.

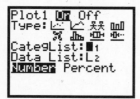

4. Set up your calculator for graphing your data. Press ⌈2nd⌉ [PLOT]. Select **Plot 1** by pressing ⌈ENTER⌉. Use the arrow keys and ⌈ENTER⌉ to turn the plot on and select the fifth graph icon, a circle graph. For the CategList, press ⌈2nd⌉ [STAT] and scroll down to find your list named PLNTA. Press ⌈ENTER⌉ twice. Insert TOTA for Data List. Choose **PERCENT.** Always press ⌈ENTER⌉ to make your choices. Press ⌈GRAPH⌉.

 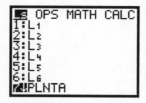 

5. Use ⌈TRACE⌉ and the arrow keys to view the labels and numbers for each sector. Notice that the calculator has calculated the percentage for you.

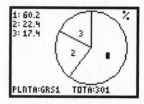

6. Repeat steps 4 and 5 to set up Plot 2 for Site B.

Size Limits of Cells

When you look at a leaf under a microscope, you notice that is made of small, rectangular structures—cells. A plant cell constantly absorbs substances it needs to live and gives off waste products through its cell membrane and cell wall. The rate at which these processes can happen depends on the surface area of a cell or group of cells. If the surface area of a cell is too small for a given cell volume, the cell cannot take in substances fast enough to survive. Also, if wastes cannot be released fast enough, they can build up and damage the cell. In this lab, you will use bouillon cubes to model cells. When the cube is placed in water, the cube begins to dissolve into ions. The released ions increase the ability of the water to conduct electricity. By measuring the water's conductivity, you will observe how fast the ions are being released.

What You'll Investigate

- How does the surface area of cells affect the rate at which substances can be absorbed and released?
- How does the surface area of cells limit the size of an individual cell?

Goals

Calculate cell volumes and surface areas.
Measure the change in conductivity of solutions over time.
Compare the rate at which conductivity increases for various solutions.

Materials

CBL 2 or LabPro unit
TI graphing calculator
link cable
DataMate program
conductivity probe
400-mL beaker
distilled water
3 bouillon cubes (1 whole,
    1 cut into two equal pieces,
    1 cut into four equal
    pieces)
metric ruler

Safety Precautions 🥽 🧴 🖐

- **CAUTION:** Never eat or drink any substances used in an experiment.
- The conductivity probe is fragile. Handle it carefully.
- Wear safety goggles and a lab apron during this lab activity.
- Wash your hands before leaving the lab area.

Pre-Lab

1. Define electrical conductivity.

2. Predict how the number of conducting particles in a solution affects the conductivity of the solution.

3. If a solid is broken into many smaller pieces, how will the rate at which the number of particles entering or leaving the solid be affected?

 SCI 1.a. Students know cells function similarly in all living organisms.

Probeware Activity 1 (continued)

Procedure

Part A: Preparing the CBL System

1. Set up the calculator and CBL 2 unit, as shown in **Figure 1.** Set the range on the conductivity probe to 0–20,000 µS. Plug the conductivity probe into channel 1 of the CBL 2 unit.

2. Turn on the calculator and start DataMate. Press [CLEAR] to reset the program. The conductivity sensor should automatically be recognized. If not, turn to page *vi* for instructions on how to set up the probe manually.

Figure 1

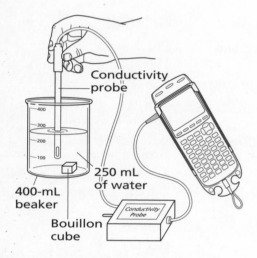

Part B: Collecting Data

1. Using a metric ruler, measure the length, width, and height of a bouillon cube in centimeters. Write these dimensions in **Data Table 1** and in **Figure 2.**

2. Pour 250 mL of distilled water into a 400-mL beaker. Gently place the cube into the water.

3. Lower the conductivity probe into the water until it is about 1 cm above the cube. Select **START** to begin the three-minute measurement.

4. Gently swirl the conductivity probe in the water. The open end of the probe should be submerged but not hitting the bouillon cube.

5. After the measurement has ended, remove the probe and rinse it in distilled water. Set it aside carefully.

6. Press [ENTER] to go to the main screen. Select **TOOLS.** Then select **STORE LATEST RUN.**

7. Repeat steps 2–6 with two cube halves.

8. Repeat steps 2–6 with four cube quarters. The time measurements will be stored in List 1 (L1). The conductivity measurements will be stored in L4 (whole cube), L3 (two cube halves), and L2 (four cube quarters).

Part C: Graphing Data

1. From the main menu, select **GRAPH.** A graph will appear on the screen.

2. Press [ENTER]. Select **MORE.** A menu will appear that will allow you to select the desired graph.

3. Select **L2, L3, AND L4 vs L1.** A single graph with three curves will appear.

4. Sketch and label this graph in the space provided on the following page. Be sure to label the curves *whole cube*, *halved cube*, or *quartered cube*.

5. When you are finished with the graph, press [ENTER]. Select **QUIT.** Follow the directions on the calculator screen.

Cleanup and Disposal

1. Turn off the graphing calculator and disconnect the conductivity probe and CBL 2.

2. The conductivity probe is fragile. Carefully rinse and dry the probe.

3. Clean and return all equipment as directed by your teacher.

Probeware Activity 1 (continued)

Sketch of Conductivity Graph

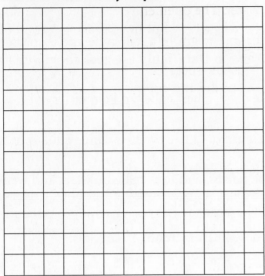

Figure 2

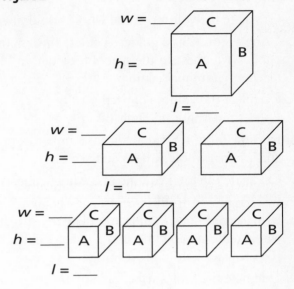

Data Table 1: Calculating Total Volume

	Length (cm)	Width (cm)	Height (cm)	Volume of One Piece	Number of Pieces	Total Volume of All Pieces
Whole cube						
Halved cube						
Quartered cube						

Data Table 2: Calculating Total Surface Area

	Area of Side A (cm²)	Area of Side B (cm²)	Area of Side C (cm²)	Total Surface Area of One Piece	Number of Pieces	Total Area of All Pieces
Whole cube						
Halved cube						
Quartered cube						

Probeware Activity 1 (continued)

Part D: Analyzing Data

1. Calculate the volume of the whole bouillon cube ($V = l \times w \times h$).

2. Using **Figure 2** as a guide, calculate the length, width, and height of a half cube and a quarter cube. Write these in the spaces provided in **Figure 2** and in **Data Table 1.** Check these with your teacher before proceeding.

3. Calculate the volume of each type of piece—a whole cube, a half cube, and a quarter cube. Enter these values in **Data Table 1.**

4. In **Data Table 1,** write the total number of pieces that are obtained when a whole cube is halved and when a whole cube is quartered.

5. Calculate the total volume of a whole cube, two cube halves, and four cube quarters and write these values in **Data Table 1.**

6. Using **Figure 2** as a guide, calculate the surface areas ($SA = l \times w$) of sides A, B, and C of a whole cube, a half cube, and a quarter cube. Write these in **Data Table 2.** Check these with your teacher before proceeding.

7. Calculate the total surface area of a whole cube, a half cube, and a quarter cube using the formula: Total SA = 2A + 2B + 2C. Why is the surface area of each side multiplied by two?

8. In **Data Table 1,** write the total number of pieces that are obtained when a whole cube is halved and when a whole cube is quartered.

9. Calculate the total surface area of a whole cube, two cube halves, and four cube quarters and write these values in **Data Table 1.**

Conclude and Apply

1. Compare the total volumes of the whole cube, the halved cube, and the quartered cube. Explain your observation. Compare the total surface areas of whole cube, the halved cube, and the quartered cube. What do you observe?

_____

_____

2. What do you observe about the conductivity of all three bouillon-cube solutions as time progressed? Explain your observations.

_____

_____

3. Explain the differences between the three conductivity curves. Which curve shows the fastest rate of dissolving? Explain your observations.

_____

_____

4. Which will allow a greater volume of substances to move into and out of a cell in a given amount of time—one large cell or an equal volume of several smaller cells? Explain.

_____

_____

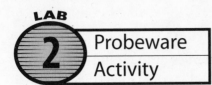 

LAB 2 Probeware Activity

Exercise and Heart Rate

Your heart is a pump in your chest that works all day, every day. It is part of your cardiovascular system, which also includes your blood vessels and blood. The cardiovascular system transports oxygen, food, and cellular products, such as insulin, to cells in your body. It also carries away cellular wastes. The systems of the human body strive for equilibrium. They work together to maintain normal conditions inside your body. During exercise, your muscles use more oxygen and generate more carbon dioxide than normal. Your brain senses this change and increases your breathing and heart rate to deliver oxygen-rich blood more quickly. When you finish exercising, your breathing and heart rate slow down. The heart rate of a physically fit person increases less during exercise and returns to normal more quickly than that of a less fit person.

One way you can investigate your heart's health is to count the number of times your heart beats in one minute. You may have done this before by lightly resting your fingers on your neck or wrist. It is called "taking your pulse." In this lab, you will use an electronic heart rate monitor. You will investigate the heart rates of you and your classmates while at rest and while exercising. You will use a graphing calculator to display and analyze your data.

What You'll Investigate

- What is your resting heart rate?
- What effect does exercise have on your heart rate?
- How long does it take your heart rate to return to normal after exercise?

Goals

Collect heart rate data.
Observe and measure the effect of exercise on heart rate.
Compare and analyze heart rate data using statistics.

Materials

CBL 2 unit
TI graphing calculator
link cable
DataMate program
hand-grip heart rate monitor
saline solution in a dropper
   or spray bottle
stopwatch

Safety Precautions

- Inform your teacher if you have any health condition that might be aggravated by physical exercise.
- If during the exercise portion of this activity you feel dizzy, faint, or unwell, stop to rest and tell your teacher.
- Wash your hands before leaving the lab area.

Pre-Lab

1. Predict your own heart rate in beats per minute.
2. Examine the heart rate monitor. How do you think it works?
3. How can you compare the data for the whole class?

 SCI 6.j. Students know that contraction of the heart generate blood pressure and that heart valves prevent backflow of blood in the circulatory system.

Probeware Activity 2 (continued)

Procedure

Part A: Preparing the CBL System

1. Set up the calculator and CBL 2 unit, as shown in **Figure 1**. Plug the heart rate receiver into channel 1 of the CBL 2 unit.

Figure 1

Receiver

2. Turn on the calculator and start DataMate. Press CLEAR to reset the program. The heart rate monitor should be recognized automatically. If not, turn to page *vi* for instructions on how to set up the probe manually.

3. Select **SETUP** on the DataMate main screen to set up the time interval between data points and the length of time the data will be collected.

4. Press the up arrow once until the cursor is beside the **MODE** line. Press ENTER.

5. Select **TIME GRAPH.** Select **CHANGE TIME SETTINGS.** The screen will display "Enter time between samples in seconds."

6. Press 5 ENTER. The screen will display "Enter number of samples."

7. Press 1 0 0. Select **OK.** Select **OK** again. The calculator and CBL 2 unit are ready to obtain a heart rate reading every 5 seconds for 500 seconds.

Part B: Collecting Data

1. Grasp the handles of the Hand-Grip Heart Rate Monitor. Place the fingertips of each hand on the reference areas of the handles (see **Figure 1**).

2. The left hand grip and the receiver are both marked with an alignment arrow. When collecting data, be sure that the arrow labels on each of these devices are in alignment and that they are not too far apart. The reception range of the plug-in receiver is 80–100 cm, or about 3 feet.

3. Sit down. Have a partner hold the CBL 2 with the attached receiver module of the monitor. The receiver must remain within 80 cm of the transmitter.

4. Sit quietly for one minute to establish normal pulse and to ensure that the monitor is working.

5. Your partner should select **START** on the graphing calculator and start the stopwatch at the same time.

6. Sit quietly for 150 seconds.

7. When 150 seconds have elapsed, begin to exercise by stepping up onto the step and down again. Always place one foot and then the other completely on the surface of the step and floor. Exercise at a relaxed, even pace for 150 seconds.

8. When 150 seconds of exercise have elapsed, sit and rest quietly for 200 seconds. The graphing calculator will display a graph when the time is complete.

9. Sketch this graph in your **Science Journal.** Include a title, labels, and units for the *x*- and *y*-axis.

Probeware Activity 2 (continued)

Part C: Examining the Data

1. Return to the main screen by pressing ENTER.

2. Select **ANALYZE.**

3. Select **STATISTICS.**

4. Press ENTER to select the beginning of the initial resting phase. Use the right arrow key to select the end of the resting phase at about 150 seconds and press ENTER.

5. Record the MEAN resting heart rate, rounding to the nearest whole beat per minute (BPM).

6. Press ENTER. Select **STATISTICS.**

7. Use the arrow keys to select the beginning and end of the exercise period. Press ENTER.

8. Record the MEAN exercise heart rate, rounding to the nearest whole beat per minute.

9. Press ENTER. Then select **RETURN TO THE MAIN SCREEN.** Select **GRAPH.**

10. Use the right arrow to move to the highest point on the graph.

11. Record the y-value (maximum heart rate) and x-value (time) that the maximum occurred.

12. Use the right arrow key to find the time when your heart beat had returned to its normal resting rate (to within 3 BPM).

13. Record this time. Then subtract the time of maximum rate to calculate your actual recovery time.

14. Calculate your maximum exercise heart rate and your exercise intensity level using the formulas in **Data Table 1.**

15. Repeat parts **B** and **C** for other members of your group.

16. When you are finished, press ENTER. Select **MAIN SCREEN.** Select **QUIT.** Follow the instructions on the calculator screen.

Data Table 1: Heart Rate Monitor Experiment

Student:	A	B	C
Mean resting heart rate (mean BPM over the first 150 seconds)			
Mean exercise heart rate (mean BPM over the second 150 seconds)			
Maximum heart rate (BPM)			
Time at maximum heart rate (seconds)			
Time of return to mean resting heart rate (seconds)			
Recovery time (seconds)			
Maximum exercise heart rate (MEHR = 220 − your age)			
Exercise intensity level (%) = (exercise heart rate/MEHR) × 100			

Cleanup and Disposal

1. Turn off the calculator. Unplug the receiver module from the CBL 2.

2. Return the heart rate monitor and CBL 2 system as directed by your teacher.

Probeware Activity 2 (continued)

Conclude and Apply

1. Describe the effect that exercise had on your heart rate.

_____

_____

2. Share data with your classmates for resting heart rate, exercise heart rate, and recovery time. Design a data table to organize this information.

3. With your lab partners, divide the responsibility for constructing a histogram of the class data for each variable: resting heart rate, exercise heart rate, and recovery time. Your teacher may give you directions for using the graphing calculator to do this.

4. Determine the minimum, median, maximum, mean, and mode for each data set from the class. Record these in **Data Table 2**. Your teacher may give you directions for doing this with the graphing calculator.

Data Table 2: Class Statistics

	Resting Heart Rate (BPM)	Exercise Heart Rate (BPM)	Recovery Time (seconds)
Minimum			
Median			
Maximum			
Mean			
Mode			

5. You can visually display information such as you have in **Data Table 2** using a box plot. Your teacher may give you directions for making a box plot using your graphing calculator. Compare and contrast this method of displaying data with the "data table method" used in Question 4.

6. What can you conclude about heart rate among members of your class?

_____

_____

7. Research to find information about the assessment of physical fitness and improving physical fitness. Write one to two paragraphs reflecting on your own physical fitness. Include data from this activity. Set a specific goal for yourself related to maintaining or improving your cardiovascular health.

LAB 3 Probeware Activity

Cooking with Bacteria

Usually you think of bacteria as something that can make you sick. But some types of bacteria are useful in food preparation. When cabbage is salted and kept in a closed container, bacteria in the cabbage cause it to ferment and become sauerkraut. The salt kills some bacteria but the sauerkraut-producing bacteria on the cabbage survive. In this activity, you will conduct a 24-hour measurement to compare how fast lactic acid is produced during the fermentation of raw cabbage and cabbage that has been boiled.

What You'll Investigate

- How can bacteria help in food production?
- How does the amount of bacteria affect the rate of lactic acid production during the fermentation of cabbage?

Goals

Measure the change in pH during the fermentation of cabbage.

Hypothesize what is responsible for the production of lactic acid during the fermentation of cabbage.

Materials

CBL 2 or LabPro units (2)
TI graphing calculators (2)
link cable (2)
DataMate program
AC power adapters (2)
pH probes (2)
ring stand (2)
test-tube clamps (2)
250-mL beakers, sterilized (2)
400-mL beaker

wash bottle
glass stirring rod
shredded raw cabbage
shredded boiled cabbage
distilled water
tongs (2)
non-iodized salt
plastic food wrap
aluminum foil

Safety Precautions

CAUTION: Never eat lab materials.
- Wear safety goggles and a lab apron during this lab activity.
- Wash your hands before leaving the lab area.

Pre-Lab

1. In the production of sauerkraut, the natural sugar in cabbage is broken down into lactic acid and carbon dioxide. What organism is responsible for this process?

2. As lactic acid is produced during the fermentation process, will the pH of the cabbage solution rise or fall?

3. How would boiling the cabbage affect the amount of lactic acid that is produced?

4. Hypothesize how the graphs of pH would differ if you measure the pH change in raw cabbage placed in salt water and boiled cabbage placed in salt water.

 SCI 7.a. Select and use appropriate tools and technology (including calculators, computer, balances, spring scales, microscopes, and binoculars) to perform tests, collect data, and display data.

Probeware Activity 3 (continued)

Procedure

Part A: Preparing the CBL System

1. Set up the calculator and CBL 2 units, as shown in **Figure 1.** Connect each CBL 2 unit to an AC power adapter. Plug each adapter into an outlet. Plug the pH probes into channel 1 of each CBL 2 unit. Turn on the calculators and start DataMate. Press CLEAR to reset the program. The pH probes should be recognized automatically. If not, turn to page *vi* for instructions on how to set up the probes manually.

Figure 1

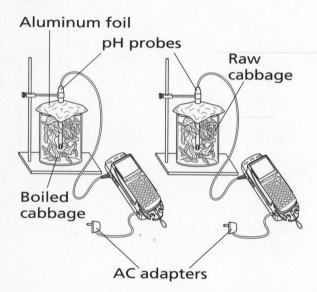

Aluminum foil

pH probes

Raw cabbage

Boiled cabbage

AC adapters

2. Select **SETUP.** Press the up arrow once until the cursor is beside the **MODE** line. Press ENTER.

3. Select **TIME GRAPH.** Then select **CHANGE TIME SETTINGS.** The calculator will ask you to input the time between samples in seconds. Press 1 8 0 0. Then press ENTER.

4. The calculator will ask you to enter the number of samples. Press 4 8. Then press ENTER.

5. Select **OK.** Then select **OK** again. The calculators and CBL 2 units are now ready to record pH readings every 1800 seconds (half hour) for 24 hours.

Part B: Collecting Data

1. Prepare a salt solution by mixing 10 g of salt in 400 mL of distilled water.

2. Using sterilized tongs, place boiled cabbage into one of the 250-mL beakers. Using another set of sterilized tongs, place raw cabbage into the other beaker. Fill both beakers to the 200-mL mark with cabbage. Then fill both beakers almost to the brim with salt solution.

3. Cover the beakers with plastic wrap, then with a square of aluminum foil. The plastic wrap and foil should have a small hole in the center to allow a pH probe to fit through it.

4. Remove the storage solution bottles from the pH probes. Slide the o-ring and cap up the sensor barrel, out of the way. Over a sink or empty beaker, use a wash bottle of distilled water to thoroughly rinse the probes. Attach the probes to the ring stand and place the ends of the probes in the solution in the beakers. Wrap extra foil around the end of the probe to keep the setup as clean as possible.

5. Wait a few minutes to allow the pH readings to stabilize. Select **START** on each calculator to begin the 24-hour measurements. A screen will appear that tells you to press "enter" to continue. Press ENTER. The calculators may be removed now. The CBL 2 units will continue collecting data.

6. After 24 hours, when the data collection is complete, reattach the calculators. Press ON to turn them on.

7. Start DataMate. A screen will appear reminding you that data has been collected. Press ENTER to go to the main screen. Select the **TOOLS** option. Select the **RETRIEVE DATA** option. A graph of the data should appear. Sketch and label the graphs in your **Science Journal.**

Probeware Activity 3 (continued)

Part C: Examining Data

1. For each graph, return to the main screen by pressing ENTER.

2. Select **ANALYZE.**

3. Select **STATISTICS.**

4. Press ENTER to select the beginning of the pH graph. Use the right arrow key to select the end of the pH graph. Press ENTER.

5. Your calculator will display the minimum and maximum pH values. Determine which of these is the initial pH and which is the final pH. Round these values to the hundredths place and record them in the **Data Table.**

6. When you are finished, press ENTER. Select **RETURN TO MAIN SCREEN.** Select **QUIT.** Follow directions on the screen.

Cleanup and Disposal

1. Remove the pH probes from the beakers of cabbage. Use distilled water in a wash bottle to rinse the probes thoroughly and place them in the storage-solution bottles.

2. Turn off the graphing calculators and disconnect the pH probes and CBL 2 units. Follow your teacher's instructions for disposing the contents of the beakers.

3. Clean and return all equipment as directed by your teacher.

Data Table: pH Changes of Raw and Cooked Cabbage

Type of Cabbage	Initial pH	Final pH	pH Change
Cooked			
Raw			

Conclude and Apply

1. Compare the pH graphs for the raw and boiled cabbage. Determine the pH change of each by subtracting the initial pH from the final pH. Why were the pH changes different?

_____

_____

_____

2. Compare your results to your hypothesis in **Pre-Lab** question 4. Explain the source of any differences.

_____

_____

_____

Notes

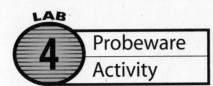

Sweat is Cool

Probeware Activity

The human body needs to maintain an internal body temperature of about 37°C to survive. When the body becomes too hot it begins to perspire, or sweat. Tiny sweat glands in the dermis layer of your skin secrete a fluid that contains water, salt, and wastes. This fluid absorbs heat from the body as it evaporates, cooling the body. In this lab you will observe how evaporation of a liquid is a cooling process.

What You'll Investigate

- Is heat removed from the environment during the evaporation of a liquid such as during perspiration?
- How can this loss of heat be observed?

Goals

Observe the temperature change as a liquid evaporates.
Interpret the data that is collected during the evaporation of a liquid.

Materials

CBL 2 or LabPro unit
TI graphing calculator
DataMate program
link cable
temperature probe
1/2 coffee filter
   *filter paper
   *cotton ball
   *cotton gauze
small rubber bands
250-mL beaker
electric fan
isopropyl alcohol

Alternate materials

Safety Precautions

- Wear safety goggles and a lab apron during this lab activity.
- Possible danger from electrical shock. Clean up spills immediately.
- Extinguish all flames during this activity. Isopropyl alcohol is flammable.
- Wash your hands before leaving the lab area.

Pre-Lab

1. Where does the heat energy needed for a liquid to evaporate come from?

2. What measurement can be observed that shows this heat transfer?

3. Explain how perspiring cools your body.

4. What are some situations that can cause your rate of perspiration to change?

SCI 7.c. Communicate the logical connection among hypotheses, science concepts, tests conduced, data collected, and conclusions drawn from the scientific evidence.

Probeware Activity 4 (continued)

Procedure

Part A: Preparing the CBL System

1. Set up the calculator and CBL 2 unit, as shown in **Figure 1**. Plug the temperature probe into channel 1 of the CBL 2 unit.

Figure 1

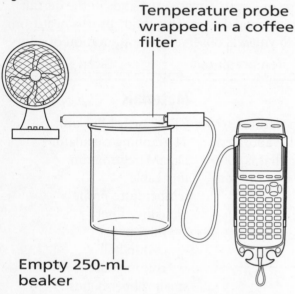

Temperature probe wrapped in a coffee filter

Empty 250-mL beaker

2. Turn on the calculator and start DataMate. Press CLEAR to reset the program. The temperature probe should be recognized automatically. If not, turn to page *vi* for instructions on how to set up the probe manually.

3. Select **SETUP** on the DataMate main screen to setup the time interval between data points and the length of time the data will be collected.

4. Press the up arrow once until the cursor is beside the **MODE** line. Press ENTER.

5. Select **TIME GRAPH.**

6. Select **CHANGE TIME SETTINGS.** The screen will display "Enter the time interval between samples in seconds." Press 1 5 ENTER. The screen will display "Enter number of samples." Press 4 0 ENTER. The CBL 2 unit will collect data every 15 seconds for 10 minutes (600 seconds). Select **OK** twice to exit. The setup screen appears.

Part B: Collecting Data

1. Using the room-temperature water that your teacher provides, put 50 mL of water into the 250-mL beaker.

2. Fold the coffee filter into a strip approximately 2 cm wide. Wrap it around the temperature probe and secure it with a small rubber band.

3. Wet the coffee filter by dipping it into your cup of water. Use care when wetting the filter and do not get water on your lab table. Wipe up spills immediately.

4. Place the probe across the top of an empty beaker, as shown in **Figure 1,** to support it during the experiment.

5. Place an electric fan 40 cm from your probe. Turn the fan on low and position the airflow so that it flows across the wetted filter.

6. Select **START** to begin collecting data.

Part C: Examining the Data

1. After data collection is complete, sketch and label the graph shown on the calculator screen in your **Science Journal.** Return to the main screen by pressing ENTER.

2. Select **ANALYZE.**

3. Select **STATISTICS.**

4. Press ENTER to select the beginning of the temperature graph. Use the right arrow key to select the final temperature. Press ENTER.

5. The calculator will display the minimum and maximum temperatures. Determine which of these is the initial temperature and which of these is the temperature after the liquid has evaporated—the final temperature. Record these in the **Data Table.**

6. Press ENTER. Select **RETURN TO THE MAIN SCREEN.**

7. Repeat parts B and, steps 1–5 of part C using isopropyl alcohol.

8. When you are finished, press ENTER. Select **RETURN TO THE MAIN SCREEN.** Select **QUIT.** Follow the directions on the screen.

Probeware Activity 4 (continued)

Cleanup and Disposal

1. Turn off the graphing calculator and disconnect the temperature probe and CBL 2 unit.

2. Put the solid waste into the container designated by your teacher.

3. Return all equipment to the proper location as directed by your teacher.

Data Table: Temperature Changes Due to Evaporation

	Initial Temperature	Final Temperature	Temperature Change
Water			
Alcohol			

Conclude and Apply

1. Find the temperature change for each substance by subtracting the initial temperature from the final temperature. Record your results in the **Data Table.**

2. What energy exchanges occurred during the evaporation process?

_____

_____

_____

3. How is the evaporation process in this lab similar to perspiration in the human body? How is it different?

_____

_____

_____

4. Perspiration occurs under heavy clothing in cold temperatures. Why is it beneficial to wear undergarments that wick the moisture away from the surface of the skin?

_____

_____

_____

5. What differences do you observe in the time-temperature graphs for alcohol and water?

_____

_____

_____

Notes

The Formation of Caves

Many processes form caves. Powerful waves carve sea caves in rocks located next to the ocean. Lava flowing from volcanoes forms caves if the surface lava cools and hardens before the lava underneath stops flowing. The most common type of cave forms when underground layers of rock, such as limestone, are dissolved by acidic groundwater. In this process, rainwater absorbs carbon dioxide as it falls through the air. As the water seeps through the ground, it absorbs more carbon dioxide in soil pores. The rainwater becomes acidic because water and carbon dioxide form a weak acid known as carbonic acid. When this acidic water reaches bedrock, it seeps through cracks, dissolving the rock and creating open areas. Slowly, over many thousands of years, the water creates a cave in the rock. In this activity, you will demonstrate the effect of increasing the amount of carbon dioxide in water. The carbon dioxide in your breath will react with the water, similar to the way rainwater reacts with carbon dioxide as it falls to Earth and seeps through the soil.

What You'll Investigate

- How does an increase in carbon dioxide affect the acidity of water?
- How does the acidity of water lead to the formation of caves?

Goals

Predict how increasing the carbon dioxide in water will affect its acidity.
Measure the change in acidity of water as you exhale into it.
Analyze a graph to determine what chemical change has taken place.

Materials

CBL 2 or LabPro unit
TI graphing calculator
link cable
DataMate program
pH probe
timer
distilled water
600-mL beaker
wash bottle
plastic drinking straw

Safety Precautions 🧤 🥽 👋

- Wear safety goggles and a lab apron during this lab activity.
- Wash your hands before leaving the lab area.

Pre-Lab

1. Describe how rainwater can contribute to the formation of a cave.

2. Describe how the pH scale is used to determine whether a substance is basic or acidic.

3. Suppose you determine that a substance has a pH of 6. An hour later, it has a pH of 2. Has the acidity of the substance increased or decreased?

4. Predict how exhaling through a straw into water would affect the acidity of the water. Explain your answer.

SCI 4.a. Students know Earth processes today are similar to those that occurred in the past and slow geologic processes have large cumulative effects over long periods of time.

Probeware Activity 5 (continued)

Procedure

Part A: Preparing the CBL System

1. Set up the calculator and CBL 2 unit, as shown in **Figure 1**. Plug the pH probe into channel 1 of the CBL 2 unit. Turn on the calculator and start DataMate. Press CLEAR to reset the program. The pH probe should be recognized automatically. If not, turn to page *vi* for instructions on how to set up the probe manually.

Figure 1

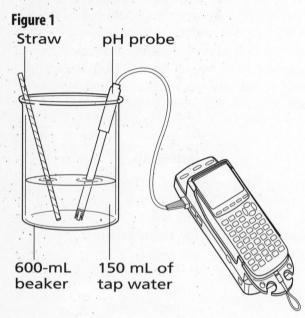

Straw   pH probe

600-mL beaker   150 mL of tap water

2. Select **Setup.** Press the up arrow once until the cursor is beside the **MODE** line. Press ENTER.

3. Select **TIME GRAPH.** Then select **CHANGE SETTINGS.** The calculator will ask you to input the time between seconds. Press 5 ENTER.

4. The calculator will ask you for the number of samples. Press 1 2 0 ENTER.

5. Select **OK.** Then select **OK** again. One pH reading will be collected every 5 seconds for 600 seconds (10 minutes).

Part B: Collecting Data

1. Put 150 mL of tap water into the 600-mL beaker.

2. Remove the pH probe from the storage-solution bottle. Slide the cap and o-ring up the barrel of the probe to move them out of the way. Over a sink or empty beaker, use distilled water in a wash bottle to thoroughly rinse the probe. Set the solution bottle aside in a location where it will not be disturbed. Place the pH probe in the 600-mL beaker.

3. Allow the pH probe to remain in the water for one minute until the readings stabilize. During this time you will be able to see the pH reading on the top right corner of the calculator screen.

4. Be sure the timer is set to count up. Select **START** on the calculator to begin the 10-minute measurement. When you hear the tone indicating the measurement is beginning, start the timer.

5. When 30 seconds have passed, use the straw to exhale into the water for 30 seconds. Cup your hands over the beaker as you exhale to ensure that water doesn't splash out onto the calculator. Do not try to exhale continuously. Inhale through your nose and exhale through the straw at a natural pace.

6. After exhaling for 30 seconds, allow the pH probe to remain in the water, undisturbed for the remainder of the 10-minute measurement.

7. A graph showing changes in the water's pH during the measurement period will appear on the calculator screen. Sketch and label this graph in your Science Journal.

8. Use the right and left arrow keys to move the cursor along the data points. The time (x) and the corresponding pH (y) values will appear at the bottom of the screen. Write the selected values in the **Data Table.**

9. When you are finished, press ENTER. Select **QUIT.** Follow the directions on the screen.

Probeware Activity 5 (continued)

Data Table: Selected pH Values

Time (s)	pH
0	
100	
200	
300	
400	
500	
600	

Cleanup and Disposal

1. Turn off the graphing calculator and disconnect the pH probe and the CBL 2 unit. Rinse the end of the probe with distilled water and place the probe in the storage-solution bottle.

2. Follow your teacher's instructions for disposing of the contents of the beakers and returning all equipment to proper locations.

Conclude and Apply

1. Describe and explain what your graph looks like between 0 and 30 seconds.

_____

_____

2. Describe and explain the curve of your graph after 30 seconds.

_____

_____

3. Explain how the results you obtained in this activity are similar to what happens when caves form.

_____

_____

_____

_____

Notes